DEFECTS OF THE HEART

DEFECTS OF THE HEART

Barbara Gordon

1817

HARPER & ROW, PUBLISHERS, New York

Cambridge, Philadelphia, San Francisco, London
Mexico City, São Paulo, Sydney

FIRST EDITION

Designer: Jane Weinberger

Library of Congress Cataloging in Publication Data

Gordon, Barbara
    Defects of the heart.

    I. Title.
PS3557.O654D4 1983   813'.54   82-48144
ISBN 0-06-015032-7

83 84 85 86 87 10 9 8 7 6 5 4 3 2 1

For Jimmy Pollock

 **ONE**

Jessica stood alone at the curb, her long white gown and black velvet evening coat little protection from a harsh, late March wind. She was searching for a taxi in competition with a doorman across the street who was waving aggressively and blowing his whistle, the sound pitifully shrill and small against the roar of traffic. The street was clogged with cars, people off to the theater, dinner parties, rush-hour stragglers on their way home. The energy of the city that was so pervasive by day, that pulsated like an infernal machine, was, at dusk, slightly muted. But tonight, not even the cold could diminish her sense of expectation.

An old woman crossed against the light, holding up a feeble hand to stop a truck with the audacity and determination required of a New Yorker. Jessica stepped off the curb and raised her hand. A taxi jumped the light and swerved to her side of the street. The doorman shouted indignantly as she climbed in and the cab started with a lurch. "The Summit Hotel, please," Jessica said. "Fifty-second and Lex." When the driver's gray-pallored face glowered at her through the rear-view mirror, she realized she had betrayed some unwritten code. He was a New York cab driver, and damn it, he didn't need directions. Shouting doormen, imperious pedestrians, belligerent cab drivers, all fiercely protecting their piece of turf. She had learned to live with, and even admire, them.

It was her city, too. Her work as a filmmaker had taken her to every corner of New York—from dimly lit factories in Chinatown where children and old women worked furtively at night, to the bowels of Grand Central Station where in the early dawn hours she had filmed the bag ladies shrugging off sleep as they collected their parcels and shuffled out onto the city streets.

Tonight was different. She was not on assignment. She was winning her first award. It wasn't an Oscar or an Emmy but in some ways it was sweeter. The American Civil Liberties Union was presenting Jessica Lenhart with a plaque praising her as the documentary filmmaker who, as the citation read, "most consistently and brilliantly deals with the great constitutional questions of our time." And it was true, she thought, at least the "consistent" part. For five years she had filmed injustice in its countless disguises, aiming her cameras as if they were cannon, trying not merely to capture it, but to obliterate it.

The cab jolted to a stop. "Here it is, lady," the driver said, turning around to collect his fare. "The Summit Hotel, just where you said it was."

Hordes of people stood drinking and chattering, jammed together in voluntary intimacy despite the size of the Summit ballroom. As Jessica pressed through the crowd looking for a familiar face, jumbled words swirled around her. Shop talk: "The *Times* wouldn't print anything before the verdict comes down. That would be prejudicial. But I know they'll go with it when the jury returns. They've been good on this issue." Strange bedfellows, she thought, journalism and law.

Small talk: "The tennis court will cost fifteen grand, but it'll net me five more in rentals." It was a black-tie dinner but the man wore an open-necked shirt that revealed a tuft of dark hair and thick gold chains. A young woman smiled at him with approval. The look on the face of an older woman nearby was one of borderline desperation. Observing them, observing the men who turned to look at her, Jessica felt more confident than ever in her own good judgment, the more fortunate in her own kind of happiness.

How much of the way she felt, she wondered, was revealed in her expression? Her dark auburn hair, brushed back on the sides and held securely by two tortoise-shell combs, framed a face that seemed to hold no secrets. Her gaze was open and direct. But the corners of her mouth, permanently turned upward in a smile, projected a kind of bemusement, as if she knew something no one else knew. She seemed secure, invulnerable—unusual for a woman of thirty-five who had arrived, and intended to leave, alone. She sometimes thought she should not look so totally taken. "Follow the advice of William James," her good friend Kate had warned her, "and always keep a window open in the attic." Her window was closed, Jessica knew, but her attic was filled with light.

A deep voice and a strong arm around her waist, and there was Mel Shane, a civil liberties lawyer with a cosmic reputation, her good friend and benefactor, the man who had provided the inspiration for four of her best films. Tall and bearlike, with a rumpled and unfinished look even in a tuxedo, he scooped her into an embrace, then held her at arm's length for a better perspective.

"You look beautiful, Jess. You should be working in front of a camera, not behind it. Why don't you try reading the weather for a living?"

"You know my station is much too classy to have a weather girl," she said. "We have a meteorologist, male, with a PhD. I need an idea for my next film, Mel, not a new job."

"Another film already? Your last one aired only a few weeks ago. What's the rush? Relax. Tonight is for happiness, not work."

"They are not mutually exclusive," Jessica said. "You of all people know that."

He grinned in agreement and then lowered his head to whisper into her ear, a habit that came from a lifetime spent murmuring to clients, hiding his words from juries and opposing counsel. "I'll come up with something. Have I ever failed you? Just accept your award and feel wonderful. You're sitting next to me and Wanda on the dais. I'd better see if I can find her. She's coming straight from the beauty parlor. Wonder what color her hair will be tonight?"

He disappeared into the crowd to look for his wife and Jessica continued to search for her own private cheering section, people from her station who were somewhere in that noisy room. Table 152. But since the tables were not arranged in numerical sequence, knowing how to count was no particular advantage. Although Lyman Ellis, the president of the station, had bought the tickets, she knew he wouldn't be there. An award presented to one of the filmmakers in the documentary unit, a small and often troublesome corner of his domain, was worthy of his notice but not his presence. But her boss, Ben Nevins, was coming and, finally, at the far end of the room, she saw him. There was someone sitting at the table with him, a woman she didn't know.

Ben rose and extended his hand. "Jessica," he said, "this is my wife, Sara."

"I'm very glad to meet you," Sara Nevins said. "Ben has told me so much about you. And I've seen most of your films, of course. Congratulations on your award."

Jessica felt her cheeks flush. "Thank you, Mrs. Nevins."

"Sara, please."

"Have some bad champagne, Jess, compliments of Lyman Ellis," Ben said. "It'll come out of the budget for your next film, so you might as well enjoy it."

Sara was a small woman with short, blond hair almost imperceptibly turning gray, a woman who emanated a softness, a pliancy that served as a perfect foil for her husband's gruff cynicism. There was no artifice in her face, in the clothes she wore, in the simple gold wedding band around her finger. "What's the subject of your next film?" she asked.

"Now you're beginning to sound like Ben," Jessica said. Uncertain of how far she could go with her boss's wife, she kept her voice light. "He's been hounding me about that for the last two weeks."

"You're damn right. We've got an open date with your name on it and it's only sixteen weeks away."

"You have another fan in our family," Sara said. "Our daughter Susanna. She's majoring in film journalism."

"In college?" Jessica asked.

Sara interpreted Jessica's surprise as a compliment. "She's

nineteen. Our son is twenty-one. Ben and I have been married for almost twenty-three years."

Was it a simple statement of fact, Jessica wondered, or was Sara, too, defending her territory, a lioness prowling the parameters of her lair?

Ben stood up abruptly. "Come on, Jess, I'll walk you to the dais. It looks like things are getting started."

The noise and confusion of the crowd began to subside as people found their seats. Jessica and Ben threaded their way through the narrow aisles separating the tables. "Have you got your speech?" he asked.

"Prepared but not memorized," she said. "I wish we could sit together, Ben. This award is yours as much as mine. If you hadn't supported me, backed me on every film I've made, I wouldn't be here."

Resting his hands lightly on her shoulders, he kissed her on the cheek. "No. This is your moment, Jess. I'm proud of you. You done good."

She found her seat on the dais behind a pile of red and yellow carnations, watching Ben as he returned to his table and his wife, and for a moment she felt terribly alone. This was an evening for people in pairs. Ben had spoken often of his wife, but until now her only physical reality for Jessica was a silver-framed photograph on his desk that must have been taken ten years ago. They lived in the suburbs, an odd choice for a man like Ben, she thought, a journalist who fed, just as she did, on the energy of the city. It was as if he wanted to keep that part of his life, that part of himself, separate, denying the realities of his profession as the photograph on his desk defied the passage of time. She had no husband, no children, no family photographs on her desk, and Jessica knew that a woman sitting alone on a dais, even if she were about to receive an award, was still considered an aberration, a freak.

"I found her, but I damn near didn't recognize her." Mel had returned with Wanda in tow. Tall, willowy, and very beautiful, she wore a gold dress that clung to every curve of her body and made negotiating the steps to the dais difficult. Tonight Wanda was a brunette. Her hair, her makeup, her clothes proclaimed her preoccupation with pursuits of the body. But she wore large black-rimmed glasses. No designer frames, no contact lenses. She slipped into the seat next to Jessica, fixed the glasses firmly on her nose, and began to read the program.

"So who else is here from your station?" Mel asked, squeezing his large frame into a small gilded chair. "Where's your boss?"

"In the back," Jessica said, "over there, on the left."

Wanda pushed her glasses down on her nose and peered over the rims into the crowd. "Who's that with him?"

"His wife," Jessica said.

Wanda's eyebrows arched expressively. "Do you notice anything different?" she asked Jessica, flashing the huge blue-white diamond she was wearing among the many other rings on her right hand.

"It's beautiful," Jessica said. "Mel, it's perfectly beautiful."

"Mel had nothing to do with it," Wanda said matter-of-factly. "You don't make that kind of money as a do-good lawyer. You're looking at textile money. My first husband was short on conscience and long on cash. I finally persuaded Mel to swallow his pride and let me wear it."

Jessica felt the warmth and good humor of their relationship. Mel's familiarity with the Constitution had not guaranteed him one moment of domestic tranquility—at least not until he married Wanda. She was the third Mrs. Shane and Jessica remembered how she had dreaded meeting her. If she were anything like her predecessor, she would love the lawyer and be totally bored by the law, her conversation focused on the vital question of whether Bloomingdale's or Sloane's had the best selection of country French furniture, the sort of woman whose inner life was so barren, her only signature was her brand of perfume. And her first sight of Wanda, who had decorated her new Park Avenue apartment as lavishly as she decorated herself, was not very reassuring. But Jessica quickly saw that where it counted, Wanda's mind was uncluttered and her vision, behind those no-nonsense spectacles, clear. "I'm glad you're winning this award, Jessica," she said. "You keep them honest."

"I have your husband to thank for that."

"I wouldn't be surprised," Wanda said. "He's not above bribing a judge or two in a good cause."

"I resent that," Mel said. "Sure, I whispered in a few ears, but all the committee had to do was look at your films. And if you really want to thank me, keep your speech short so we can get out of here. And for God's sake, don't eat the food. We're going to a great little French restaurant in the Village. There's someone from the office I want you to meet."

"You might have let *me* in on your plans," Wanda complained. "I'll be a big hit in Greenwich Village in this outfit."

Jessica knew instantly that Mel was up to something. "You've got a new case," she said. "Can I use it for my next film?"

"Maybe yes, maybe no. I've turned the case over to this guy and he can be pretty bull-headed. He might not exactly welcome the prying eyes of a television camera. Likes to do things his own way."

"That," Wanda said, "could only be Doug Weber."

"Then you've told him about me?" Jessica asked.

"All about you, sweetheart. So I might as well tell you something about him. Columbia Law, used to make a lot of money doing some corporation's dirty work until he saw the

light. So now he's working for me. A little rough around th
edges, but I think you'll like him, Jess. And he's single."

"You *must* be kidding," Wanda said. "Jessica and Doug

"Don't worry. It's only the story I'm after," Jessica sai

"I'm sure that's not all Mel has in mind," Wanda replie
wryly.

"Hell, you can't blame me for trying," Mel said with
broad grin.

"And I suppose," Wanda added with a sigh, holding he
huge diamond to catch the light, "there are worse thing
than getting mixed up with a lawyer."

Jessica felt a little ridiculous cradling the large, elaboratel
engraved plaque in her arms as she followed Mel and Wand
to a corner table in the tiny French restaurant. "I'm sorry
madame," the checkroom attendant had told her, "we can
be responsible for trophies."

"That's the French," Wanda said, trying to make hersel
comfortable on a slippery plastic banquette. "They've neve
taken responsibility for anything. How do we get somethin
to drink? I don't want to slide under this table cold sober.

Jessica laid the plaque on the empty chair beside her, an
Mel had just given their orders for drinks when she notice
that his jovial expression suddenly changed to a smal
frown. A man had appeared at their table, and he was no
alone. His arm was anchored with prideful possessio
around the waist of a striking young woman.

Mel recovered his composure quickly. "I see you foun
the place," he said. "You know Wanda, of course. And thi
is the lady I was telling you about. Jessica Lenhart. Doug
Weber."

"Wanda, Miss Lenhart," Doug said, and then he pre
sented his own trophy. "This is Bambi Littrell. We'll need
another chair."

The waiter brought it and Doug very deliberately seated Bambi next to Jessica. "Does this belong to somebody?" he asked, holding up her plaque.

"Sorry. That's mine," Jessica said.

"Very impressive." His tone was condescending.

Jessica took the plaque and for a moment wondered what to do with it. Then she eased it to the floor and rested it against the legs of her chair. From the fleeting look of disapproval on Mel's face, the table for four that now held five, she knew Bambi Littrell had not been part of his plans for the evening, and suspected that Doug, mistrusting Mel's motives, had taken precautions to protect himself. Bambi was protection for her, too. But here she was again, an extra woman, odd in a world of evens.

Doug Weber was a handsome man: thick, curly hair, coal black eyes under heavy brows, strong, sloping shoulders. He knew he was attractive to women: the lines of his mouth told Jessica that. The set of his jaw told her that he could use it, if he thought it necessary. "Rough around the edges"— that was Mel's phrase. And he was. The sweater he wore under a tweed jacket probably dated back to his days as an undergraduate. No tie, but no gold chain around his neck either. Those rough edges were carefully studied, yet there was a brusque intensity about him that seemed quite spontaneous. He could play it both ways, Jessica decided, and then found herself surprised that she had even noticed his eyes, his open shirt.

With the alacrity of a slick trial lawyer confronted by an unexpected piece of evidence, Mel turned his charm on Bambi, extolling the virtues of the restaurant and the food. "Wanda and I found it by accident a couple of months ago and we've been coming here ever since."

Bambi's face brightened. Until that moment she wasn't sure which of the two women at the table was Mel's wife.

All through his discourse on artichokes vinaigrette, she had kept her eyes on Doug and Wanda. Now she had it straight: the one with the glasses belonged to Mel, the lady with the plaque belonged to no one, and Bambi was relieved. Wanda could have been competition. Jessica was attractive, but dressed almost primly, her dark hair drawn back from her angular face, she was no threat.

Mel summoned the headwaiter and, after a long and serious discussion, set about telling his guests what they had to eat. "Darling," Wanda said wearily, "let people order what they want." But that wasn't Mel's way and it might have been offensive if he were not so genuinely concerned with giving pleasure. Jessica trusted him completely. Wanda complained but complied. Only Doug asserted his independence by ordering an entrée of his own choice. Bambi, who wished to make it clear that she was no stranger to fine French food, said merely, "No *champignons* for me, Mr. Shane. I'm allergic."

Bambi's hair was long and streaked with several shades of blond, and the subtle coloring of her eyes and cheeks had a professional touch. The voice was low, the gestures languid. Probably a model, Jessica thought, who wanted to be an actress, and she wondered, again to her surprise, how many Bambis there were in Doug Weber's life.

"I hear you're on television," Bambi said, turning to Jessica.

"Not exactly on," Jessica replied. "In. I make films."

Bambi was disappointed. "Then I don't suppose you'd know any producers or directors."

"As I understand it," Doug said, "Jessica *is* a producer, Bambi, and a very good one. There can't be too many women in your field, and even fewer who maintain an ongoing relationship with the Bill of Rights."

"Yes, it's a love affair, me and the First Amendment," Jessica said. "And Mel regularly plays Cupid."

When the wine appeared, Mel sniffed the cork, swirled and sipped, enjoying the rituals of dining as much as the food itself. But that was not the only reason he had arranged this evening. "To Jessica," he said raising his glass. "An oasis in a vast wasteland."

"To television," Doug added. "It sure moves merchandise."

To Jessica, his criticism was a familiar challenge. She was not a defender of the faith, but she believed implicitly in what she did. "Television does indulge a few people like me to move an idea from time to time," she said.

"Not often enough," Doug replied. "We can write off most of commercial television as chewing gum for the eyes, but doesn't your station claim to be something more? It isn't, and I think I know why. It's become part of the system, not outside it, scrutinizing, criticizing, asking questions. How can television investigate the government that pays its bills? Or the corporations that rape the planet, gouge the consumer, and then buy a little goodwill with a grant to your station for an evening at the ballet? How can anyone take money from oil companies and then make a film about the stranglehold they have on our lives?"

"You can't," Jessica said. "You give them English drama for their money. You do my kind of film with someone else's dollars."

"Dollars have strings attached. Payment for services rendered."

"Of course," Jessica said. "But you learn how to snip the strings. I've never been told what to film or what not to film."

"Probably because you've never tried to take a good healthy bite of the hand that feeds you."

His argument had shifted from a criticism of television to an attack on her own integrity, and Jessica would not conceal her annoyance. "And who pays your bills?" she asked tartly. "Public interest law firms get government grants and money from rich lawyers with guilty consciences. Just as many strings attached. How does that affect the kind of work you do?"

The thin line of Doug's mouth broke into a smile. "You could be right. Maybe we're both tokens allowed to paddle around in our little ponds as long as we don't make too many waves. The prosecution rests."

"Well, I agree with Doug," Bambi said with a flip of her golden hair. "I think television is infantile." Shifting slightly in her chair, she placed her hand on Doug's leg and began to caress his inner thigh.

Jessica noticed Bambi's hand. She saw Mel incline his head toward Wanda to whisper something in her ear. And for an instant, she felt like a child, her nose pressed against a window, smudging the glass, outside of all that was happening, a spectator, an observer. At moments like this, she judged that feeling harshly, as a flaw. But her profession nourished it, required it, and she was here to do a job. So she reverted to her professional self, panning the table, zooming in on Wanda, pulling back on Mel, freezing the frame on Doug. She had disarmed him and he didn't even know it. Nothing could touch her when she was working.

They were sipping coffee when Mel saw the evening coming to an end without having accomplished its main purpose. "You know," he said, "the McCampbell thing might be something Jessica could run with."

The expression in Doug's dark eyes changed. He had underestimated Mel as usual. There was something more on his mind than just a romantic liaison with this complacent media lady. "It's too soon, Mel," he said. "That kind of publicity would send everybody diving for cover."

"Maybe so. But when Jess and I did that film on the city

insurance scam, she got to people who wouldn't even talk to me on the phone."

"You won that case, didn't you, darling?" Wanda said.

"And the city is still playing the same old dirty tricks," Doug remarked. "So much for the power of the electronic eye. No, Mel. You said I could handle the case my way, and my way, for the moment, has no room for cameras."

Jessica decided it really didn't matter. How could she work with a man who allowed himself to be stroked by a Bambi? Maybe, she consoled herself, the case was too obscure and high-principled even for public television. "I really must go," she said. "Mel, Wanda, thank you for everything. Bambi, Doug, nice meeting you." She pushed back her chair, knocking over the plaque at her feet.

Doug picked it up and presented it to her with a small bow. "This is yours, madam. I didn't mean to give you such a hard time. If you're going uptown, we can all share a cab."

"Thanks," Jessica said, "but I live just a block or two away." She had taken only a few steps from the table when she heard Bambi's throaty voice. "Why did you offer to share a cab?" she asked peevishly. "Women like that always go home alone."

∽TWO∽

"It's the same old stuff. Boring." Jessica tossed the papers back to Ann Berris who sat at a nearby desk already buried in papers. "Overcrowded prisons, slum lords, consumer ripoffs . . ."

"The Defense Department stuff isn't bad, Jessie," Ann said, her blue saucer eyes peering through the blond bangs that drooped over her forehead.

"We pitched it last year," Jessica reminded her, "and Lyman wasn't buying. Two months later the *Times* did the story, remember?"

"What else is there?" Ann said. "Mental patients, battered children? The same stories, the same characters."

"The same victims," Jessica murmured, her eyes gazing around their cramped office. Books, magazines, and newspapers were piled on the floor. Film cans and stacks of video cassettes, audio tapes, records, and slides lined the shelves. Clippings, correspondence, transcripts bulged from the drawers of a filing cabinet. She was surrounded by the debris of her past films. Ben Nevins had once remarked, "Walking into this office is to be reminded of all the sins of commission and neglect of a society gone mad." When Ann first came to the station as Jessica's assistant, she had balked at working in such chaos; it violated her New England sense of order. But Jessica had worn her down by example.

Ann was on the phone to a friend at a Boston affiliate. "Yes, I know we live in Sodom and Gomorrah but what's going on up there? Anything we can use? Judges on the take? No, we've done that. Even Catholic corruption? Look, we're desperate."

"Who's McCampbell?" Jessica asked.

"Football coach?" Ann ventured. "Scottish racing car driver? I give up. Who?"

"That's just it, I don't know. I don't even know if it's a he. I met a man last night, Doug Weber, Mel Shane's protégé. He's working on a case that involves a McCampbell, and Mel thought it might make a film, but he shot us down. It seems he despises television—and women who have something more important on their minds than the care and feeding of Doug Weber."

"One of those," Ann said. "Doesn't he know he's an endangered species? McCampbell? You want me to check? We might have something in the library."

Before Jessica could answer, Ann was up and out of the

office, carefully closing the door to protect their cluttered hideaway from the prying eyes of the station brass. Shortly after Lyman Ellis assumed command, he had ordered a major overhaul of the station. An effete interior designer was hired to supervise the job and his first act was to sweep away the relics of the more boisterous days of public television. Cigarette-scarred desks, swivel chairs, and sagging sofas disappeared overnight, replaced by vinyl, chrome, and glass. A memo for general circulation read: "No plants, posters, and personal mementoes are permitted. And leave the furniture as you find it, please. We are striving for symmetry and dignity."

"Conformity and blandness," Jessica had remarked, as she and everyone else at the station packed up their possessions the afternoon before the facelift. It was like a Russian purge. When they returned the following morning, green-white fluorescent lights hummed relentlessly in an airless, sterile environment. There was nothing Jessica could do about it until she was given an office of her own with a window she could open and a door she could close. The station's studios had been used to tape soap operas and five dollars slipped to the janitor got her into the basement prop room where she found an antique desk lamp that had once graced the set of "The Edge of Night." Another five and the janitor dimmed the blinding overhead light. She kept a thorny cactus named Max on the window sill during the day and tucked it away in a desk drawer at night, in case the cleaning woman reported her to the management. And Ann, soon after she moved in to share the office, added her own personal protest: a giant poster of Robert Redford thumbtacked to the back of the door. "If Ralph Nader looked like that," Jessica had quipped, "we could move mountains."

This morning her mood was grim, the elation of winning

the award the night before completely forgotten. It wasn't only her meeting with Doug Weber. She had this same feeling every time she was looking for a new idea. For years she had traveled with lights and cameras through the dark tunnels of social injustice—factories, mines, rat-infested tenements, green-walled mental hospitals. There was nothing more to see, no place else to go. Why not make one last massive film about everything, she thought, a blockbuster that would annihilate all of the world's problems, then go out of business, find another job? How sweet it would be to focus on something other than the imperfections of the world.

Go out of business? It was a futile hope. She was not scrawling some obscene protest on a subway poster; her words and pictures reached millions. And there was so much more she wanted to do. But now time was running out. Her next film had already been scheduled, and today at the monthly meeting of the producers in his documentary unit, she knew Ben Nevins was going to ask her about it. She had cut it close before, but never this close.

Ann opened the door and Robert Redford disappeared against the wall. "I think the McCampbell he's talking about is McCampbell Pharmaceuticals, Maplewood, New Jersey."

"I knew it sounded familiar," Jessica said. "What do they make?"

"Everything. A whole lot of over-the-counter stuff."

"Any dirt?"

"Well, they got their wrists slapped by the FTC for truth in advertising."

"Great," Jessica muttered. "Anything else?"

"Nothing. Clean as a whistle. According to *The Wall Street Journal,* an aggressive new management team took over a few years ago and began a multi-million-dollar research and development program on the hard stuff, prescription drugs. I guess they figured that's where the real money is."

"Maybe Doug Weber is representing some disgruntled scientist in a patent suit," Jessica said sourly.

"How about political prisoners around the world, Jess?" Ann was back at her desk, riffling through newspaper clippings. "Korea, the Philippines, Argentina. Scary stuff, and we'd get to travel."

"Can't you find some problem in the south of France?"

Ann picked up the phone again, this time calling Chicago. "Jack? Annie. What's going on out there that's really horrible? Jess is under the gun and we're desperate. Wait a minute, I'll ask. Are you interested in a sewer scandal?"

"Why not?" Jessica shrugged. "The Chicago sewers. That's the only place I haven't been. How much time have I got before the meeting?"

"Ten minutes. You'll think of something."

Jessica went to the window, trying to relieve the empty feeling in the pit of her stomach. "Max is dying," she said.

"God, you're a grouch today," Ann said. "And Max is not dying. He's resting, a period of quiescence. We all need that once in a while, even plants."

"Not me," Jessica said. "I'm sorry, Annie. You know I'm always this way until we find something and start work. Always."

If he closed his eyes, it could have been seven years ago: lunch at the musty Stuyvesant Club with Lyman Ellis, public television's newest wizard and challenger to New York's powerful media elite. He felt out of place from the moment he entered the club. His regular haunts were McFeely's and Biarritz on the other side of town, where he hung out with his cronies from commercial television. It took two hours and two bottles of wine before Ellis finally got to the point. His new station, WPTN, was booming, he boasted, with soaring foundation grants, audience subscriptions, government handouts, corporate pledges, and it had become a serious rival to WNET, the long-established public station in New York. No longer would public television be the darling of a small intellectual elite, and Ellis wanted Ben Nevins to join the staff as vice president of public affairs programming.

Ben said no. His expertise was in "hard news" and Ellis's station had a midget news department. All those dollars pouring into his coffers were budgeted for "entertainment." And the salary he offered was fifteen thousand a year less than Ben was making in his present job. But Ellis knew just how to play him, knew of his idealistic bent, that he came from the tradition of journalism. And when he was promised the opportunity to build a first-rate documentary film unit, Ben reconsidered. Because ratings just didn't warrant the expense and sponsors were as hard to find as audiences, documentaries were fast becoming the dinosaurs of television. Maybe in the more favorable climate of a public station, amid the lush vegetation promised by Lyman Ellis, he could save them from extinction. He took the job.

It was a logical decision. The news on commercial television wasn't journalism. It was show business and he had stumbled into it almost by accident. After college he began his career as a stringer for one of the wire services. During the 1960s, he was a correspondent, covering events in Dallas, Watts, Salisbury, Saigon. Then in the middle of one of New York's interminable newspaper strikes, he had answered an appeal from a commercial television station to do background on a major story. A year later he was in charge of its news department.

The man who had once mocked television journalism, to whom the words were mutually exclusive, turned that lackadaisical department into the most successful operation in the city. Not by being a maverick, or even ingenious. He played by the book, the ratings book. He fired the longhairs and beards of the dying counterculture, retired the elder statesmen of a previous generation, and replaced them with handsome heads. Never mind that they knew nothing of New York, of City Hall politicians in their shirtsleeves, union leaders, precinct captains, had never felt the heat of a tenement fire, heard the deafening roar of the subway. They were not journalists, or even reporters. They were actors. He dressed them in matching blue blazers with the station logo on their breast pockets and they became six-figure media stars by covering the polar bears in the Central Park Zoo.

No, he wasn't sorry to leave that kind of journalism. And even if it was exactly what Lyman Ellis wanted for his station, he had chosen not to compete with it. Instead, he put together a small, efficient, streamlined news department, staffed by reporters and writers who were in touch with the outrageous mood swings of the city. Working for something more than ratings, he earned the grudging admiration of his old colleagues in print journalism, and regained his own self-respect.

He was even prouder of his documentary film unit. Taking what had been intended only as a dangling plum, a vague promise, he forced Lyman Ellis to make a firm commitment to documentary films. He fought, bargained, cajoled, even threatened to resign until he got what he wanted: the money to hire and support a small group of producer-directors, who, over the last few years, had turned in a string of high-quality, compelling, and controversial films.

They were a peculiar lot. Irv Seiden, the "poet of poverty," sported a tiny goatee and a beret. With oblique angles, filtered lenses, and gels, he caressed tenements with his cameras and made them sparkle in backlit sunshine. He rhapsodized slums, romanticized urban blight, transformed graffiti into a lofty form of contemporary art. His films extolled the nobility of despair, reflected a serene acceptance of the way things are. And he always brought them in under budget. Ben never had any trouble selling Seiden's work to Lyman.

Larry Higby, with the temperament of a basketball coach and the pushed-in face of a bulldog, specialized in "soft core" documentaries. Ben stole him from a commercial station, where he had ground out three-and-a-half-minute human interest fillers for the evening news. Expanding his format but not his subject matter in Ben's unit, Higby filmed only the obscure and arcane: a quilting bee in Tennessee, the man in Connecticut who grew an American flag the size of a football field with red, white, and blue asters. And because his political convictions and social comments were so adroitly sugar-coated, his films topped the documentary ratings.

Howard Tarr was the Willy Loman of the department, bitter, self-pitying, envious, a man who flourished because his films played to the so-called silent majority, chronicling its fear of life, death, and unemployment. Cops and bartenders, firemen and factory workers, men and women just like himself, took on grandeur as they soliloquized their frustrations. His work was part public opinion poll, part group therapy. For whatever personal motive or political belief, Tarr laid bare the anatomy of human nature, which Ben could defend as necessary to any form of journalism.

Then there was Jessica Lenhart, the junior member and only woman on the team. She was already there when Ben was hired, writing station break copy and subscription appeals. Their paths crossed a year or so later after she had moved to the public affairs department, one among many attractive young women who endured the low pay and long hours because of the cachet of working for public television. But there was a difference: the intense eyes, the half smile, as if she were hearing a secret joke. Ben noticed that she was always in a hurry. They nodded in hallways, exchanged a few rushed words in the cafeteria, and then Jessica asked him for an appointment. Sitting on the edge of the chair opposite his desk, her ankles crossed and her fingers intertwined, she said simply, "I want to make films."

Ben decided to be equally direct. "What's your background?"

"A BA in American literature, summer jobs as a researcher at WBBM in Chicago, assistant producer for WTLA in Atlanta, and two years in the news department at WNYC. We all got the ax when your programming began to beat us in the ratings."

"I'm sorry," Ben said.

"I wasn't, not with anchormen wielding blow dryers."

"Why public television?" he asked, checking a smile.

"A lot of reasons. I watched reporters read the morning papers for a crash course on what was happening before they met their camera crews. They had no sources, no regular beat. Expertise was reserved for sports and the weather. That says a lot about commercial television."

Ben searched his pockets for his cigarettes, then found them on his desk. "Ordinarily I look for cynicism and indifference in my department, Jessica. Your idealism, while attractive, may work against you. But I'll see what I can do."

She came to the documentary unit as a researcher assigned to whatever producer needed her services. Then, as an associate producer for Seiden, she shot her first film segment. Sick the day they were scheduled to film the emergency room at Bellevue Hospital, Seiden asked her to handle the shoot, and when the film came back from the lab, she sat with him in front of the Moviola, explaining what she had done and how it could be cut into his film. It was a painful experience. She had, she thought, tried to emulate his gauzy style, but when things suddenly got rough—sirens, stretchers, the blood, the brutality—she filmed what she saw, straight, harshly lit, recording the confusion and terror of those everyday battles for life. "It's fine, Jessica," Seiden said. But he didn't use a single frame. It was too grim, too realistic. Her *cinéma vérité* style looked freakish next to the smoothness and gloss of his work.

Ben screened the unused footage and gave Jessica her first assignment as a full-fledged producer: a nursing home in Queens. No one else in the unit would touch it. But Jessica dug in, practically living in the home for three weeks before she shot a frame of film. The results were stunning: old men and women speaking with dry eyes of their bitter confinement in the filth and stale air, juxtaposed against brittle, acid interviews with the indifferent staff. No fancy shots, no dissolves, no wipes, no music. Ben was overwhelmed.

Soon after, she began to film her own ideas and for the last five years had turned in a series of documentaries that were fearless, if not always technically flawless. Her film on Medicare fraud attracted both a rave review in the *Times* and an angry denunciation from the AMA. Her film on the adoption racket garnered no less than seven threats of legal action. For Lyman Ellis she was a perpetual aggravation, a weed in his carefully tended garden. For Ben, who fiercely defended her work no matter who criticized it, she was what film journalism was all about.

He glanced at his watch. In a few minutes his producers would assemble for their ritual monthly meeting. They were the stepchildren of his department, working in cramped quarters on tight budgets, and he wondered what they thought of his office: the thick carpet and upholstered furniture, the videotape machine and the four television monitors that permitted him to keep an eye on the competition. There was a part of Ben that missed the chaos and clattering teletypes of a pressroom. His office was a little too quiet; the atmosphere a little too rare. But he was fifty-two now, and he had grown used to it. He liked where he was.

Jessica was the first to arrive, a few minutes early as usual, and took her customary seat in the corner of the couch at the far side of Ben's office. If she was on time, she thought she was late. Larry Higby and Howard Tarr were arguing when they came through the doorway. Don Berg, the unit manager with a breast pocket full of pens and a sidepocket pulled out of shape by the weight of a calculator, walked in apprehensively, knowing he was not entirely welcome here. Jeff Russell, chief of the technical staff and the man who edited her own films, sat down on the couch next to Jessica, chomping on an unlit pipe, the sleeves of his sweater worn through at both elbows.

Irv Seiden was the last to arrive, wandering in dreamily as if his eyes were as out of focus as his films. "Hey, Irv," Larry Higby said, "hear you got a great sunset yesterday in the South Bronx."

"*Sunrise*," Seiden responded, oblivious to the irony of the remark. "And it didn't come easily. I had to wait three mornings before I got what I wanted."

Don Berg made a mental calculation of how much that was going to cost in overtime charges for the camera crew.

Tie loosened, shirtsleeves rolled, Ben preferred to look the part of working journalist, not studio executive, for these meetings. "Okay, before we get started," he said, "I'd like to announce the imminent arrival of a mystery guest this morning. Lyman is coming down to say a few words."

There were murmurs, a groan. Lyman Ellis *never* came downstairs. What was it, another budget cut? Ben held up his hands for quiet. "It has to be good news," he said, "or Lyman would send somebody else." He picked up a sheaf of production schedules. "Any changes I should know about before he gets here? Irv, why don't you start?"

Irv Seiden rose and, tugging at his little goatee, began his recitation in a voice as serene as his view of life. No problems. He sincerely believed that this film would be another cinematic masterpiece. Everything was on time and under budget. "I'll be ready with a fine cut by the fifteenth," he concluded.

"Larry," Ben said.

Larry Higby shrugged. "Nothing special. I'll be on location in Wyoming next week. The stock footage is on order and I can cut it in when I get back. I should be on time with an answer print."

Howard Tarr jumped up even before his name was called and began his familiar litany of complaints. This was the toughest film he'd ever done, the budget was too small, the camera crew too undisciplined, nobody loved him. "Of course, I'm behind schedule," he said, "but it isn't my fault. My kid fell off his bicycle and broke a leg."

"Jessica," Ben said. "What's happening?"

There was an expectant silence in the room and again Jessica felt that empty tug in her stomach. "Nothing yet," she said. "I'm looking into a couple of things."

"Don't worry," Tarr muttered sourly. "Lois Lane never misses." Jessica was not everyone's favorite producer.

"Jeff," Ben said. "Any problems at your end?"

"Just the usual," Jeff Russell said, sucking on the unlit pipe hanging from his mouth. "I don't suppose this is the time to mention what's happening to the equipment in editing. We might get more out of it by donating it to the Smithsonian as a tax writeoff."

"I know, I know," Ben sighed. "I got your memo and Don

is looking into it." He raised his hand to smooth the thinness of his hair, a momentary admission that he, too, was worried. Begging for time, for money, for equipment, for the right to exist was a continual humiliation. But his job, the jobs of everyone in the room, depended on it. "Well," he said, trying to lighten the mood, "three docs in the works and not one of you is investigating malfeasance in the House of Windsor."

Everyone roared with laughter. Public television's infatuation with things British was a joke they all shared, a bitter joke because they knew they could make at least four films for the cost of one English import.

A buzzer rang on Ben's desk and he picked up the phone. "That was Monica. She just left Lyman at the elevator. He'll be here in a minute."

"Monica's not a secretary," Jessica whispered into Jeff's ear. "She's an air traffic controller, monitoring Lyman's flights."

And then Lyman Ellis was standing in the doorway, his smoky gray hair the same color under the fluorescent lights as his three-piece tailored suit. "Hi," he said as he strode into the room. "I know you're busy so I won't take up too much of your time." He meant that *he* was busy and this courtesy call would not take up too much of *his* time.

"First of all," he continued, "I think we should congratulate Jessica for the award she received from the NAACP." No one bothered to correct him. ACLU, NAACP, initials like that were all the same to Lyman. "I would also like to offer my personal congratulations to the entire documentary unit. It's been a remarkable year for all of you. And, I certainly don't have to add, a remarkably difficult one. We're all reeling from the recent cutbacks in government funds and lagging support from subscribers. Inflation has taken a terrible toll on public television. But these are challenging times and we can rise to that challenge. Revisions in the tax laws will encourage more generous corporate grants and the Board of Governors and I are mounting a campaign to attract new funds from large companies and foundations alike. Some of that money, I hope, will go into a pool of unrestricted funds, and we all know what that can mean to every facet of public affairs programming. So thank you for your good work. I know you won't let me down in the future."

Jessica closed her eyes, permitting her imagination to enjoy her favorite fantasy of Lyman Ellis: the cheerleader trying hard to be one of the boys because he was not quite good enough to make the team. When she opened them, he was gone. Lyman did not linger, did not encourage the intimacy of comments or questions.

Irv Seiden was the first to speak after he left the room. "Would somebody please tell me what he just said?"

"It sounded like a vague promise of more money," Jessica said. "Very vague."

"You could shoot for a week," Jeff replied, "on just what he paid for that suit."

"Damn it!" Howard Tarr exploded. "Don't you know without Lyman Ellis we'd all be out on the street?"

"True," Larry Higby said. "But I've always found it difficult to kiss the ass that feeds me."

"Okay, okay," Ben interrupted, "that's enough. Howard's right. Let's give the man a little credit. So we're always the last in line. He's running the only game in town and we all know it." He stood up behind his desk, a signal that the meeting was over. Then raising his hands in benediction he said, "Let us pray that Lyman's unrestricted pool doesn't dry up before we get our feet wet. Thank you, gentlemen. Jess, do you have a minute?"

She waited as the others filed out of the office before she moved to the chair in front of Ben's desk. She knew what he wanted, and she still didn't have an idea for her next film, not one.

"Excuse me, I'm sorry to interrupt." Ann Berris poked her head through the doorway. "You got a call, Jessica. Doug Weber wants to know if you can have lunch?"

"When?"

"Today. Right now. He's trying a case in federal court and wants you to meet him downtown. Ever been to the Casa Mendoza?"

Jessica jumped to her feet. "Ben, this could be important. Can we talk later this afternoon?"

"At your leisure," he said with a shake of his head. He sat back in his chair as she grabbed her bag and rushed out of his office. That's Jessica, he thought. Always in a hurry.

THREE

Films have created the illusion that the life of an investigative journalist is a dangerous calling: drama in dark alleys,
clandestine meetings in cloakrooms, secret sources, stolen
documents. In fact, much of Jessica's time was spent in li-
braries, poring over aseptic reports written in dense bureaucratic jargon. Then there were weeks of writing letters and
making telephone calls, trying to locate an expert, a mavin,
someone who knew what was in those reports, and what
had been left out. Days following clues that led only to other
clues, or nowhere; lonely nights in motels in strange cities
waiting for the phone to ring. And endless hours in drab

diners and dreary restaurants, just like this one: bad food, cheap liquor, courting, pleading, swearing eternal friendship, eternal silence, trading a drink for a fact, a meal for a new lead—all in the name of "getting the story." For every minute of film, millions of minutes had to come before. The only real danger in her profession, as she once confided to Ben, was food poisoning. It wasn't that she was weary of it, nor even that she despaired of it. It was merely the reality of her job.

La Casa Mendoza was a rundown Mexican restaurant near the court buildings clustered around Foley Square. The two men seated at a nearby table, their faces only inches from their food, were obviously lawyers. The man who sat in solitary splendor, an empty table on either side of him, was probably a judge. There had to be restaurants in the area better than this one, Jessica thought. The awning over the door to the street was in tatters. The floor was dirty, the walls dark. A small wooden counter passed for a bar; the odors from the kitchen were overpowering. The guitarist who, according to a sign in the window, played "even at lunch" was sitting sullenly in a corner drinking beer. Was this some kind of test, Jessica wondered, an ordeal she had to pass to prove her sincerity, her worthiness to hear Doug Weber's story?

He was not there when she arrived. Half an hour later, he was still not there. Jessica sat alone, embarrassed by the suspicious stares of the waiter and the quizzical glances of the other patrons. Finally, she ordered a bottle of club soda and wondered why this sudden invitation to lunch if he wasn't going to show up. Obviously he intended to tell her something about his case. But if he didn't, she might try a little flattery, a pose of helpless innocence, a touch of wide-eyed wonder. She regretted now that there hadn't been time to change into something softer, more seductive than a turtleneck sweater and gray wool pants. her working clothes. No, she was no model, no Bambi Littrell. She would listen to whatever he had to say with her usual professional detachment, as if this were just another interview and she was looking at him through the eye of a camera.

She saw him enter the restaurant, carrying a bulging briefcase in one hand, loosening his tie with the other. For effect? To impress her as an open-throated, unfettered, unconventional male? "Sorry I'm late," he said. "And I don't have much time before I have to get back." The small table wobbled and teetered as he sat down. "What are you drinking?"

"Club soda."

"Like a tourist," he said. He summoned the waiter. "Two margaritas and two Number Five combinations and a side order of guacamole tostados. We're in a hurry." He rocked back in his chair, both hands clasped behind his head. It was, Jessica thought, a position associated with daydreaming—or indifference. An antidote to intimacy. "About last night," he began, "I didn't mean to be rude. But this case I'm working on is still in its very early stages and I'm uneasy talking to anyone outside the office about it, especially anyone from the media."

Jessica forced a smile, wondering where he was headed.

"Mel caught me by surprise when he mentioned McCampbell. Have you looked them up?"

She nodded.

"I thought so. And what did you find?"

"Nothing much, just whatever has been in the papers. I'm sure I could find out a lot more."

"I'm not so sure." The waiter brought their drinks and Doug took a long sip. "I want to be frank with you, Jessica. I owe Mel that. But just what are you after, another plaque?"

She should have expected that. Skillfully Doug was making her the supplicant, a client who might not be able to afford his fee. "I know lawyers who would kill to get on television," she said. "It's good for business."

"I'm not one of them," he said humorlessly.

His walls were still intact, drawbridge up. He was, Jessica saw, so well defended. "I'm interested in something a little more important than plaques," she said. "As a result of some of the films I've made, a law has been changed, a statute reworked. Cameras and lights have a way of focusing attention on things that might otherwise go unnoticed. And I think I'm good at what I do."

"And exactly what is that? What do you do?"

"I read, research the facts, find out everything I can about what's involved on both sides of an issue. Then I talk to people, ask questions. I can get information from anyone."

"Anyone?"

"Anyone. From people who've sworn they'd never talk, from people who talk too much without realizing what they're saying. That's the easy part. All I have to do is listen. It's much harder to get them to talk in front of a camera, particularly if they have something to hide. But I've never filmed anyone who didn't want to be filmed. And I know that journalists don't always enjoy the same rights of confidentiality as lawyers, but I've never betrayed a source."

"That's very noble," Doug said. "But what happens to the people you film, the lives you intrude upon?"

"I don't really know," Jessica replied. "It's the one part of my job I don't like. I walk in with an army of cameramen and walk out again, with very little time to look back at the wake created by my invasion. I always have to move on, make another film, fill another hour. Television is a hungry monster. You can feed it a Russian defector one week, a corrupt CIA agent the next, a Palestinian terrorist after that, and it's still there waiting, hungry. I wish the pain and injustice of the lives I film would disappear as quickly as my name in the closing credits. I have to forget that it doesn't. But after all, journalists are supposed to be impartial, unprejudiced. We can't get too involved."

"Can't you?" he asked, again leaning back in his chair.

The waiter began loading their small table with platters of tacos and tostados piled high with guacamole and runny white cheese topped by a rich red wetness. The tortillas stacked on a thick white plate were steaming hot. Doug ordered a Mexican beer which was set before him in an icy bottle.

"I don't know where to start," Jessica said.

"It doesn't matter. Just dig in anywhere." He had already begun eating without ceremony.

Jessica dipped a tortilla into the spicy sauce, then sampled a taco. "It's delicious."

"You sound surprised," he said. "I know the place doesn't look like much, but it has the best Mexican food in town. Why did you think I invited you here?"

"I hoped you were going to tell me about your case."

He was silent and Jessica heard the guitarist in the corner strumming a few soft chords to tune his instrument.

"Okay," Doug said finally. "The case is about the creation of monsters."

"Monsters?"

"That's what it's called. A teratogen, a monster-producing drug. The government has just approved and McCampbell Pharmaceuticals is about to market a monster-producing drug."

"Like thalidomide?"

"Yes, but this is a new one, at least in this country. It has some elaborate chemical name, but the trade name is Styralon and there's reason to believe its effects are even more terrible than thalidomide's. It was developed in Germany but first approved and prescribed in England."

"What's it for?"

"It's supposed to prevent miscarriages. And maybe it does. But in a significant number of cases, the children of the women who have taken the drug are born with gross malformations. Stunted or missing limbs, enlarged heads, cleft palates, punctured hearts. I can't even talk about it without feeling sick."

"But how could it happen?"

"That's what I'm trying to find out. I don't know how the laws work in England, but the procedures for approving a drug in this country are very rigid. Too rigid, some people claim. But the law is specific. Ever since thalidomide, a drug has to be proven both safe and effective. Those are the key words, and the FDA does not accept test results from abroad. The drug must be tested here. And that's where the system can break down. For the most part, the FDA doesn't conduct its own tests. It merely reviews the process and accepts or rejects the results. Testing is the responsibility of the companies that manufacture the drugs."

"You mean that McCampbell itself tested Styralon? That's incredible."

"No, it's not that clear-cut. The companies can't do it all themselves, so they hire independent labs."

"But the labs would still be on the drug company's payroll."

"Exactly. And there has to be a temptation to tell the drug company what it wants to hear."

This was it, the story she had been searching for. But she concealed her excitement. "I don't know why I'm surprised."

The guitarist was strolling toward them, strumming and crooning his version of "La Paloma."

"Surprised?" Doug said, almost shouting at her. "Goddamn it, you should be horrified! Think of the children,

Jessica. They're the ones who will pay the price for that kind of corporate collusion. I'm sorry. I didn't mean to snap at you. It's just that . . . ''

The guitarist stepped closer, picking out another romantic ballad.

Jessica ignored him. "Who are you suing?"

"McCampbell Pharmaceuticals and the United States of America," Doug said. "We're seeking to enjoin the distribution of the drug and ask the government to show cause why it should not be banned. But there's not much of a case yet. In fact, I haven't got a case at all."

"What do you need?"

"A Person with Standing."

"I don't understand."

"An injured party, a child with a birth defect and evidence of a direct link between Styralon and the mother."

"What evidence exists that it *is* a teratogen?"

"Just what I've been able to get from England. Nothing in this country yet. And that's what's so frustrating. Sometimes it takes a generation to discover the terrible side effects of a new drug. How many years, how many malformed children will be born before I can get the kind of evidence I need?"

"But how could McCampbell or the FDA ignore even the slightest suspicion that the drug might be dangerous?"

"That's just it. I don't know yet. The FDA won't be much of a problem. It's a government agency and I've already started proceedings under the Freedom of Information Act. It'll take time, but eventually I'll get what I want. McCampbell is another story. It's a corporation, and the Freedom of Information Act won't work on them. And it has an exclusive patent on the drug in this country, which is worth millions. It has no intention of giving away trade secrets."

The food between them, cold and congealing on the thick

white plates, was forgotten. Their waiter was pushing a broom around the floor of the almost empty restaurant. The guitarist was back in the corner, drinking another beer.

"How did you hear about Styralon in the first place?" Jessica asked.

"From England. A group of doctors there who suspect the drug has teratogenic side effects have been conducting tests and writing articles in the medical journals. So far their evidence has been dismissed as 'statistically insignificant.' "

"Who have you spoken to here?"

"More doctors. Some of them have heard of Styralon and the new English tests. But only McCampbell has tested it over here. I asked them for a list of the labs that had performed the tests, but that, it seems, is 'privileged information.' And any further inquiries, I was told, should be stated in the form of a letter to their legal department. So I wrote the letter, and got a printed form in return which said only that my letter had been received."

Doug leaned back in his chair. "So there you've got it. You're pretty good at getting information out of people after all. But I'm up against a stone wall, Jessica. That's why there's nothing you can do for me, nothing you can film."

"Money and power," Jessica said instantly. "And a system that allows something like Styralon to happen."

"Those are abstractions, damn it. I'm talking about people, damaged people. I can't sue a system. How in hell can you film it?"

"I'm talking about people, too. I can get them to talk to me. Forgive me, Doug, but a letter from you on legal stationery is a red flag to a company like McCampbell."

"And Jessica Lenhart, muckraking filmmaker, isn't?"

"Of course she is. But if Jessica Lenhart wanted to do a film on a new miracle drug pioneered by the wonderful people at McCampbell Pharmaceuticals, she might get through the front door."

"No, I can't let you do that. You may be terrific at cloak-and-dagger work, but first of all, I can't use any information obtained fraudulently. And second, even information you obtain legally could prejudice my case."

"I'll be very happy to leave the fine legal points to you. You can see whatever I film. You can even be present at the interviews when I find people who will talk on camera. That's the way Mel and I have worked in the past."

"The answer is still no. That's not the way I work, Jessica. I don't want you poking around in this case. At least not until I can see where it's going."

"Has it occurred to you that it might not go anywhere?"

It was the wrong thing to say. She saw him frown slightly and look at his watch. Then he signaled the waiter for the check. "I'm late. I should have been out of here half an hour ago."

Jessica reached into her bag, found her wallet, and pulled out a credit card. "Let me pay for this."

"A bribe?" he asked.

"I have an expense account," she replied wearily, accustomed to explaining, apologizing, every time she offered to pick up a check for a man.

"Sorry, Jessica, this one's on me." He took a roll of bills from his pocket and paid the waiter in cash. "Give this to the guitarist," he said. "We enjoyed the music."

She had made another mistake. First she had questioned his professional competence and now she had injured his male pride. Stupid. She had her story, but her source was slipping through her fingers. She wanted to say something more, to remind him that winning this case was more important than all the old poses and antique disguises. But he had already pushed back his chair and picked up his briefcase.

He took her firmly by the elbow, guiding her through the dark restaurant. The guitarist grinned as they passed and toasted them with his beer bottle, convinced his music had achieved the desired effect: love in the afternoon.

Outside, standing under the tattered awning, Jessica saw two old men pasted against the front of the building, trying to catch the warmth of a sharp streak of sunlight. When she saw people like that, faces upturned, moving only slightly as the sun moved, she always felt an impulse to go up to them, to tell them that spring was almost here. But she never did.

The street was empty of cabs. There was still time for one last appeal. "Doug, I know you think what I do is ineffectual and intrusive. But lawsuits aren't the only avenues of change. People must be made to see what has gone wrong in our society. And television can do that. *I* can do that."

He smiled at her, almost reluctantly. "The lady wants to get involved?"

"Yes."

A taxi pulled up to the curb and he opened the door for her. "I'll let you know, Jessica," he said, and then slammed it shut.

Ann had her feet up on the desk, holding the telephone to her ear when Jessica rushed into the office. "Where have you been?" she said. "Ben's been prowling the hall all afternoon. He wants to see you."

"And I want to see him."

"You've got something," Ann said, covering the receiver with her hand. "I can tell just by that look on your face. What is it? Did Weber come through?"

"With flying colors. If Ben likes it, we're back in business." She dumped the contents of her purse on her desk, searching for a comb.

"I knew you could do it," Ann said and then returned to her phone call. "Sorry, Larry, the used-car scam will have to wait. Jessica is onto something else."

The door of Ben's office was open but he wasn't there. Jessica sat down in the chair facing his desk, that empty feeling in the pit of her stomach gone. Trying to compose herself, collect her thoughts, she read through the notes she had made of her conversation with Doug Weber during the cab ride back to the station.

Ben walked in a few moments later and carefully closed the door before he began to speak. "I can't wait much longer, Jess, before I'll have to start reshuffling schedules. If you haven't come up with anything new, maybe I can talk to Lyman about some of the ideas he vetoed last year."

Jessica just looked up at him, that bemused smile on her face.

"I'm serious, Jess," Ben said, puzzled by her expression. "You're running out of time."

"I have an idea, Ben. A new one. Or at least I think I have. And I've never, never tackled anything like it before. So many of my films, our films, have been about one bad guy, one villain. This one would be different, more complicated, more people involved, millions of dollars at stake. But what it would really be about is children. The lives of unborn children. Hundreds, possibly even thousands of them. It would be about injury, Ben, the kind that takes place in the womb. Do you know what a teratogen is?"

He was unprepared for her rush of words, but he recognized the evangelical tone in her voice, the excitement in her eyes.

"A teratogen is a monster-producing drug. Remember thalidomide? That was a teratogen. This one is called Styralon. It's just been approved and a company called McCampbell Pharmaceuticals is ready to put it on the market in spite of evidence that it has caused gross malformations in the children of the women who have taken it."

"But that's impossible with all the new legislation and safeguards."

"That's what I thought, too, until I heard about it today at lunch. Mel Shane's law firm is preparing a case against the drug company and the government, but Doug Weber told me that so far he's been unable to get any information about how and why the drug was approved."

"Doug Weber?"

"The man I had lunch with. He's the lawyer in Mel's office who's handling the case."

"Are you saying that someone is conspiring to put this drug on the market knowing it's a teratogen?"

"Conspiracy, collusion, or merely some bureaucratic screw-up, who knows? That's what I intend to find out. But there's a problem. Weber doesn't want me interfering with his case, at least not yet."

"Interfering? Who the hell does he think you are?"

"I'd rather not talk about that. I'm sure he'll come around eventually. But why wait? Ann and I can start digging now."

Ben was standing by the window. The late afternoon sky had changed to a menacing slate gray. "I foresee a lot of problems, Jess. These drug companies play hardball. Their lawyers have lawyers."

"Come on, Ben," she said, "what's the fun of making a film without the threat of a few lawsuits?"

"Tell that to Lyman."

"Yes, I know. He'd be much happier with Irv's sunrises in the South Bronx or Whither Mass Transit. But, Ben, this isn't nickel-and-dime stuff. It's government, science, and industry—more important than anything I've ever done. And as far as I know, I'm the only one who has the story."

"What if this guy Weber is just crying wolf? There are some people who think toothpaste causes birth defects."

"Then I'll find out." She left her chair and went toward him. "You've got to say yes, Ben. You've got to let me try."

He nodded. "How can I stop you? I know that look in your eyes."

He took her in his arms, no longer an impersonal employer, no longer a brusque, hardbitten journalist. He was the man who loved her. The man she loved. She returned his kiss, but then, her hand on his chest, she pushed him away, a gentle reminder of where they were.

"It's a great idea, Jess," he said, still holding her firmly around the waist. "But it'll be rough. Are you sure you know what you'll be getting into?"

It was his favorite role: the seasoned city editor cautioning an eager young reporter off on her first assignment. "You say that every time I start a new film."

"I just don't want you to get hurt. And who is this guy Weber? How old is he?"

Jessica pulled away from him. "Ben. You're jealous."

"Damn right, I'm jealous."

"You don't have to worry about Doug Weber," she assured him. "And you'll talk to Lyman, won't you? He always makes me feel so . . . Bohemian."

"Of course I will, and if he says yes, I know exactly what will happen. You'll disappear for weeks."

"It's my job, Ben."

"Sometimes I hate your job," he said, embracing her again, kissing her lips.

The phone rang, a jangling interruption in the charged silence of the room. They drew apart and Ben picked it up, shifting gears easily, once again affecting his usual executive role. "It's Howard calling from location," he said. "I've got to talk to him. But tomorrow, Jess? It's Thursday."

"Of course."

"Okay, Howard, what's the problem this time?"

As Jessica turned to leave his office, her eye caught the silver-framed photograph of the woman on Ben's desk, the woman she had met for the first time the night before. She wished now they hadn't met, that Sara Nevins could have remained imprisoned in that frame, one-dimensional and lifeless. But it was only a passing thought, quickly erased by her expectations for tomorrow. Thursday, her night with the man she loved. And there were her expectations for the weeks ahead. The camera was zooming in. Ben, a new film, her life in perfect focus.

"So what do you think?" Mel Shane stood in the doorway of Doug's office.

"Just give me five minutes," Doug said.

"Perfect." Mel disappeared and Doug heard the sharp crack of ice cube trays on the stainless steel sink in the small kitchen down the hall. It was a tradition that had evolved soon after he came to work for Mel. As dusk took over the city, the two men sat down together in Doug's office, a bucket of ice and a bottle of Scotch between them, to sift through the day's activities before they headed out into the night.

Doug remembered another office in another building where they had first met. He was working as a corporation counsel for a firm on Wall Street and Mel Shane, the famous civil liberties lawyer, had brought suit against one of the many companies Doug's firm represented. It was a personal liberty issue. Mel's client had been asked to inform on the sexual history of a co-worker. He refused, was fired, and was now asking for compensatory damages. Little more than a routine nuisance suit in Doug's mind until Mel Shane himself requested an appointment. He ambled into Doug's office, nodded appreciatively at the lithographs on the walls, admired the panoramic view of New York Harbor, and then came directly to the point. "You haven't got a defense," he said, "and the only thing I can say about your brief is, it was beautifully typed. Who did it? I'd like to hire her."

The case was settled out of court and Mel hired Doug instead. An indifferent brief, prepared by the man reported to be a Wall Street wonder, was the only encouragement he needed. It was not a difficult courtship, a few drinks, a couple of games of handball, and he had Doug Weber in his pocket. Bored and disgusted by the practice of corporate law, Doug left that world and took a hefty cut in pay to labor in Mel Shane's vineyard of good works. Their bargain was sealed by a handshake and a smile on Mel's face that stretched from ear to ear, lighting sparks in his gray eyes. It was an expression he reserved for moments of triumph—a favorable ruling in an important case, a winning return on the handball court, his wedding to Wanda, and that night on a long plane trip when he and Doug were playing Scrabble and Mel suddenly crowed, "A seven-letter word. That's fifty points, damn it! Fifty points!" Doug called it his seven-letter smile.

"Nice girl, Wendy," Mel said, referring to the young woman who sat outside Doug's office. "She always offers to get the ice."

"I know," Doug said. "She never does, but she feels she has to make the gesture."

Mel deposited the ice bucket on Doug's desk, found glasses and the bottle of Scotch in a cabinet, and poured their drinks. "What happened in court today?"

Doug grinned. "Justice triumphed."

"Then appeal at once," Mel said. It was an old joke between them. He rattled the ice in his glass and took a gulp of Scotch. "And what's new on McCampbell?"

"Good news. Wendy handed me this. It's a list of the labs involved in the Styralon tests."

"Where did you get it?"

"Let's just say through unofficial channels. Now the problem is seeing their records."

"You can't subpoena them until you've filed suit."

"I'll figure out some other way."

Slumped in a chair, his legs stretched out before him, Mel pretended to examine his glass. "I'm sorry you and Jessica didn't hit it off last night."

Doug saw what was coming. Mel was incapable of indirection. "As a matter of fact, I took her to lunch today."

A smile, maybe two of the seven-letter version. "Where did you go?"

"Casa Mendoza."

"Christ, couldn't you think of something better?"

"She said she loved it."

"You told her about McCampbell?"

"I figured I had to after last night. And I was right. She was already nosing around. Mel, I don't want her or her cameras on this case."

"Why the hell not? We need all the help we can get."

"You know how I feel about . . . "

"About what?" Mel interrupted. "Television? I don't share your view, but that isn't the point. I know what it can do for us. What *she* can do. On the housing authority case, her film turned it around even before we got into pre-trial hearings. If you say no, then you arm the other side and rob us of one of our best weapons. We're a cockamamie do-good law firm and McCampbell has more power in its pockets than I care to think about."

Doug remained silent.

"And another thing. She's got dough for investigation, dough we can use. And she does a better job of digging than most of the guys on our staff. Give her that list of testing labs and she'll have *them* taking her to lunch. And not at Mendoza's."

"I know she's good at what she does," Doug said. "She told me."

"Then what's the problem? She's smart. She's beautiful, and believe me, I know from beautiful. I'm a fan of beautiful. And she cares."

"Maybe she does, but it's not just television, Mel. It's her. She bothers me. It's something about the way she operates. She clicks on and off like a camera."

"In other words you don't want to go to bed with her."

Doug was startled by the remark. Sometimes Mel could be too direct. "It didn't even enter my mind."

"That's what I mean." Mel reached for the bottle of Scotch and splashed another drink in their glasses. "I don't believe you. Since when does a lawyer let his personal feelings about anyone, male or female, jeopardize the outcome of a case? Let her make the film. She'll do a hell of a job."

"I'll think about it, Mel. Just give me a little more time."

Mel drained his glass and began to unbutton the old gray sweater he invariably wore in the office. "I know you hate it when I do this," he sighed. "Intrude. I hate it myself. Some day, you're going to get really pissed and walk out of here."

"And go where?" Doug asked. "Back to contracts and bond issues and cases I despised? You saved my life. I'm not here because what we do is so noble. It's totally selfish on my part. Sure, I get irritated, mad, but pissed? Not very often."

"Except when I thrust Jessica Lenhart on you."

Standing up, Mel took off his sweater and Doug noticed the slump of his shoulders, the extra weight he was carrying around his waist. He looked tired. "You're working too hard," he said. "How do you feel?"

"Never better," Mel said. "Thanks to Wanda, of course. Want a ride uptown?"

"No, thanks. I've got stuff to do here."

"Well, good night. You're the one who's working too hard."

Doug swiveled in his chair to face the window and, in a lighted office of the building across the street, watched a cleaning woman dumping wastebaskets. What was it Mel had promised when he turned the McCampbell case over to him? A free hand. That, for Mel, was impossible. He ran his law firm like the father of a large and unruly family. And with three wives and two grown sons, perhaps the role came naturally to him. But to Doug, whose father was a stranger, it was an unfamiliar relationship, as if he were being asked, at the age of thirty-eight, to catch a ball for the first time.

He had often imagined what kind of man he would like for a father: kind, uncritical, offering love without suffocation, understanding without condemnation. A father whose embrace would somehow leave both hands free. "Come, my gay Communist son. Here are the keys to the car. Your mother and I are lunching at the club. Bring your friend." Such a man was pure fantasy. And Mel was unquestionably real, intrusive, incapable of such diffidence. He could not conceal his passion for principles, nor his impatience with anyone who opposed them. His love was never uncritical; his embrace rarely left even one hand free. It often seemed to Doug that Mel was trying to mold him into some reincarnation of himself, just like a father. And like a son, Doug felt he had to resist.

"Will there be anything else, sir?" Wendy entered his office, her voice mimicking the secretaries of another time.

Doug spun around in his chair. "No, my dear, there's nothing. This time, just make sure the mink coat goes to my mistress, and the roses to my wife, pick up my shirts at the laundry, and you might consider washing these glasses."

"I'll consider it," Wendy said. It was another nightly ritual, this mockery of office ghosts. They performed the old boss and secretary routine as a joke because a new routine was not yet reflexive. Wendy was very good at it; Doug didn't find it quite so easy. Sometimes he thought it might be nice to have a secretary who *would* pick up his shirts.

"There is one thing," he said. "Those labs in the McCampbell case. Can you find out who runs them?"

"Before or after I finish your appeals brief on the Board of Education case?"

"I get your point. After. Thanks, Wendy, and good night."

He looked at a desk piled with file folders, letters, legal briefs. "Damn," he said aloud, slamming his fist on the desk. The lingering taste of the Scotch in his mouth was bitter. Time, money, Mel, the horror of Styralon. And Jessica Lenhart. Intrusions. If he could use her, why should it matter what he thought of her as a woman? Still, for a moment, he wondered who she went to bed with, what she was like in bed. Cool, distant, demanding, clicking on and off, her passion somewhere else. He erased the picture from his mind. Maybe there was something she could do on the McCampbell case. But in the private places of his own life, no more Jessicas. Not again.

FOUR

S he stood with a cup of coffee in her hand, inspecting the apartment. She had changed the linen on the bed. The usual chaos in which she flourished had been transformed into manageable disorder. Sunlight flooded through the one window with a view—the Washington Square arch and a tiny segment of the park beyond. She wished she could see more of the city, a vista sweeping from river to river, with a border of buildings, reds and yellows blending into shades of clay, that looked as if it were made of papier-mâché. She wanted to be that high. It would match her mood this morning, the way she felt every Thursday morning.

Ben loved her small apartment, the tumult of her Greenwich Village neighborhood, vivid contrasts to the bland expanse of his suburban existence. They met here before dinner to make love when all their senses were starved, then walked to a quiet restaurant to dine, to talk, before returning to make love again. It seemed so right: the touching, the tasting, the fresh linen, the large velour towels. They listened to Mozart and sipped Amaretto from the old snifters she had found in a shop on Second Avenue. While he showered, she made coffee, an aromatic French roast, and he drank it, standing at the door, before he took her in his arms to say goodbye, his attaché case bouncing lightly against her back. Her Thursdays were like a weekend crowded into a few evening hours, a feast spread out on a huge table set for only two, the whole of love and life compressed into a small, safe place.

Her plaque from the ACLU was still propped up on the hall table, and she thought of Doug Weber, so different from Ben, testy, defensive, guarding some anachronistic citadel of masculinity, viewing her, not himself, as the incongruity. His style was modern—the open collar, the uncombed hair. But in an electronic world, he was a battered old radio, spilling out static, his wires crossed between selfishness and a sense of self.

Jessica had known too many men like that. Her father, for one, who was not an anachronism, merely typical of his time. While his insurance business was run in partnership, his marriage was a closed corporation in which he was the principal stockholder. Tenderly, he made his wife Beryl a satellite, held securely in orbit by the gravity of his needs, an ornament wrapped in cotton as carefully as the small jewel he presented her for every anniversary. Like one of her mother's plants, Jessica had thrived in the heat and light of her parents' devotion. She adored her father. For three years she loved and had almost married a man exactly like Jack Lenhart.

Plants. Somehow the plants she kept on the window sills of her apartment always looked as if they were gasping for air, engaged in a life and death struggle for survival. Nothing she tried, read, or fed them seemed to work. They languished and eventually died. When her mother came to visit, she always brought cuttings and sturdy seedlings from her own verdant collection with specific instructions for their care. "It's useless, I know," she once said, looking at a terminal philodendron, "bringing anything green to New York. How *you* manage to survive is a mystery."

It was like Beryl to blame New York, not her daughter, for the death of her plants. After all, not everyone was blessed with her gift for keeping things alive. But that gift, as it must, had failed when Jack Lenhart, at sixty-four, only a year before he planned to retire, suffered a fatal stroke. No one could have saved him, but Beryl blamed herself. She had not loved him enough, cared for him enough. In midnight phone calls and long, incoherent letters, she poured it all out to Jessica, every tiny slight and unwitting injury of their almost forty years of marriage. Jessica's grief, her own loss, was overwhelmed by her mother's guilt.

Friends did what they could for Beryl. The house in Chicago was sold and, leaving all her plants behind, she moved to an apartment. There, her center of gravity lost, she seemed to spin aimlessly in even that small space. How could she refashion a life without Jack, with Jessica in New York? For her, it would be like trying to furnish a fifty-room mansion on Social Security.

The torrent of phone calls and letters continued, and after a visit to New York which ended with Beryl in bitter tears, Jessica sought help. She met Kate Marchand for the first time in her apartment overlooking Central Park. The sun-washed room that served as the office was crowded with plants as lush and exuberant as her mother's. She was a handsome woman with a face framed by thick gray-black hair. But it was her hands, with strong fingers and blunt nails, that caught Jessica's attention, hands that she used forcefully, continually, for emphasis, for punctuation. Jessica trusted her instantly.

"My mother is dying," she said. "Without my father, her life is empty. It has no meaning, as if someone had stolen into the park and pulled the plug, draining the reservoir of every drop of water."

"And you feel you have an obligation to fill it?" Kate asked.

And so Jessica began to speak of herself, as the adored only child of Beryl and Jack Lenhart, not just the brightest, but the single star in their constellation. As if she were filming her own life, she searched for pictures, freeze frames to describe it. Beryl and Jack sitting under a brightly colored beach umbrella. A Christmas vacation in Florida, Jessica's first glimpse of the ocean. Bored by her pail and shovel, she trundled toward the breaking surf, shrieking with glee as the waves washed over her legs, nearly knocking her down. Her father raced to pick her up, grabbing her under the arms, sitting her on his shoulders, high above the threatening waves. She indulged his fears, playing in the hot sand near the umbrella for a while, and then made for the ocean again. Her father caught her, pulling her back. Beryl laid her embroidery down and, with a serene smile, reached out to them, a hand for Jessica, a hand for her husband, drawing them toward her in a magic circle. "I can remember the sweet vanilla smell of suntan lotion," Jessica said, "but not a word. It was a scene played in pantomime. Underneath that umbrella, I would always be safe, enveloped in a love that ruled out all injury, all pain."

Another picture. Her mother at the window of their house, the curtain drawn back, waiting for her father to come home, while Jessica set the table. Fiesta Ware, each piece a different color: a tangerine plate, a cucumber green cup on a saucer of pumpkin yellow. Finally, he came trudging up the walk, exhausted from a day of selling insurance, and they rushed to greet him at the door, take his briefcase, hang his hat and coat in the hall closet. And then they sat down at the table, just the three of them, bathed in a circle of white light. She could remember the dishes, the light, Jessica told Kate, but she could not recapture a sound, a syllable of what was said around that dinner table. It was a silent film. "My father traded in death and disaster in other people's lives," she said. "But we would always be secure. Eternally happy. Immortal."

"And now the circle is broken," Kate said. "It happens to all of us and in time we make other connections."

At the end of the hour as Jessica prepared to leave, she asked, "How do you do it? Your plants. They're beautiful. Mine wither and fade away. I remember the first time Ben was coming to my apartment. I was so ashamed of my plants that I rushed to the florist and brought home armloads of fresh flowers. The place looked like someone had just died. That was before I realized he would love me in a desert. But I still do it. Every Wednesday night, I plunder the flower shops in my neighborhood."

"Old habits die hard," Kate said. "The same time next week?"

In later meetings Kate persisted in talking about Jessica, not her mother. "And what do you want for yourself?" she asked. "Another umbrella? Your own circle of white light?"

"I thought I did. But I'm not so sure, now that I've seen what my father's death has done to my mother."

"Perhaps even before," Kate said. "How long have you been seeing a married man?"

Jessica bristled. "Why do you assume he's married?"

"You plunder the flower shops only one night a week."

"I don't see what that has to do with my mother or her marriage."

"Does she know?"

Fighting her resentment that Kate was encroaching on territory she did not want her to enter, Jessica said, "For over a year I couldn't bring myself to tell her about Ben. And then one night, I was so happy, I blurted it all out. She was outraged."

Kate's strong hands made a gesture of acceptance. "What did you expect?"

Jessica told her another story, a short film, this time with dialogue. On Beryl's last visit to New York, she stayed as usual at a hotel near Jessica's apartment. But most of her hours were spent cleaning, shopping, and cooking for her daughter, trying to bring order to her life, the part she could see, the part she could touch. Her conversation was a litany of the medical miracles that had saved the lives of her friends. "It was cholesterol," she said, sponging the white enamel of the refrigerator with baking soda and water, "but they did a double bypass and now Charley's playing golf twice a week just as he always did." Her meaning was implicit: somewhere in the world there was a brilliant surgeon, a pill, a course of treatment that could have saved Jack Lenhart.

Beryl had taken to wearing jangling jewelry since her husband's death, gold bangles around her wrists that announced her comings and goings like the bell on a cat. It was,

Jessica decided, a hopeful sign, an affirmation that she still existed and made some noise as she moved through life, even if there was no one around to hear it.

At the dinner table she said, "Don't you want some more of this veal ragout, darling? You know it's always been your favorite."

Beryl got up, bracelets jangling, to clear the table. "No, don't you move. You've worked hard all day. I've got a little surprise for you." She returned from the kitchen and presented her daughter with a gaily wrapped package.

"What is it, Mother? It isn't my birthday."

"It's something I know you need."

Jessica unwrapped the package while her mother rewound the ribbons and carefully folded the paper as she always did. It was a shiny toaster with one slit.

Jessica tried to conceal her astonishment. "Where in the world did you find a one-slice toaster?"

"I got one after your father died. This one is exactly like it."

"But what if I want to make a sandwich?"

Beryl pursed her lips in an expression of injury. "If you don't want it, I'll take it back."

"No, Mother, I'll keep it. We both have breakfast alone."

"If your life were different, I'd gladly buy you a toaster with six slits," Beryl said. "But until . . ."

"You mean until I get married?"

"No, I don't mean that at all. Marriage isn't the issue. I'm not one of those mothers who doesn't know what's going on these days. But at least if you lived together, you'd have someone here for breakfast."

"He's a marvelous man, Mother."

"But you deserve more."

"I'm fine. I'm happy."

"What about his wife? Is she happy? What does she deserve?"

"She has a great deal. She has most of him."

"That's my point," Beryl said, tears filling her eyes. "You settle for crumbs."

"He's a banquet for me, Mother, not crumbs."

"Well," Beryl said, sniffing and drying her eyes on a napkin, "there are some things I'll never understand."

They had played this scene before, Jessica told Kate. It had become a necessary ritual during her mother's visits. Only the toaster was new. But happily, once it had been performed, the script could be put aside. Beryl had made her comment on Ben Nevins.

"She knows when to get off," Kate remarked.

As it turned out, Beryl also knew when to climb back on. "An encouraging report from the front," Jessica announced just a week or so later. Central Park was covered with the first snowfall of the season and a hard winter light angled through the windows of Kate's office. "My mother writes that friends have invited her to come to Florida and she wants to go. But she's unhappy about leaving all her new plants."

"It was only a question of time," Kate said. "You forget, Jessica, that your mother had the strength to let you go. What would you like to talk about now?"

"Ben?" It was a question.

"Whenever you're ready."

Jessica looked past Kate's luxuriant plants to the bleak winter landscape of Central Park. "May I call you?"

"Of course."

"I don't mean as a patient. Would that be ethical?"

"Probably not." Kate paused, studying Jessica's reaction. "But I've got an even better idea. My husband and I are giving a dinner party next Sunday night. I think you and Paul would have a lot to talk about. Can you come?"

"I'd love to."

They embraced, Jessica tentatively at first, until she felt the strength of Kate's hands on her back. It was a signal that they were friends.

"Thank you," Jessica said. "Maybe you'll meet my mother some day."

"That would be fine. But not breakfast at your place."

Did Kate suspect what her weekends were like, Jessica wondered? Saturdays were easy, tolerable. She shopped, visited the galleries, went to movies and plays, did all the things people in New York do on Saturday with their friends. On occasion, she even went through the rituals of a date which, at her age, she thought slightly absurd. But pleading fatigue, she always left the man standing in the lobby of her building with a slightly puzzled expression on his face and went to bed alone.

Sundays were the worst, a desert of unremitting loneliness. She tried never to think about them in advance. But in the middle of a Sunday afternoon, when the day already seemed to be twelve hours long, she sometimes drew the curtains of her apartment, creating a shadowy haven from the sunlight, pretending it was night and the weekend was almost over.

She went to Kate's party and met her husband Paul, a writer and peripatetic journalist who, it turned out, had known Ben Nevins for years. His name came up often in their conversations that evening, again on later occasions. Paul's good-humored remarks betrayed no knowledge of Jessica's relationship with his old friend. He merely chided her for always being alone. Kate had kept her secret. Only in her eyes, whenever they kissed hello and goodbye, did Jessica see the tiny question marks that meant, "Are you ready to talk about it now?" And her reply, punctuated by the small periods in her own eyes, was always, "Not now, not yet."

She took one last sip of her coffee before pouring the rest of it down the drain. The one-slice toaster on the kitchen counter was not as shiny now, less a recrimination than a symbol of her mother's kind of love. For if nothing else, Beryl was extremely practical.

In the hallway Jessica folded the *Times* into her tote bag to read on the bus uptown. And throwing her coat over her arm, she took a final look at the apartment. There were fresh flowers everywhere except the bedroom. That's where she would put the coral roses Ben brought with him religiously. They usually lasted through the desert of her weekends. But why think about that? Today she would find some way to penetrate Doug Weber's defenses. She would woo him and win.

And tonight there was Ben.

Through the thickness of his morning mind, he remembered it was Thursday. Yawning and stretching, he got out of bed and walked slowly to the bathroom. As he shaved, he examined his face in the glass, a face creased with lines of experience, he told himself, not etched with age. He ran his hand up his cheek. Dissatisfied, he shaved again.

In the shower, water thumping on his back, he counted the years of his life he had measured out in Thursdays. How many fictitious editorial meetings had kept him in New York until the last train home? Yes, he was a middle-aged man with wrinkles and incipient bulges. He had watched it all happen gloomily, saw parts of him grow sparse where he most wanted thickness and fullness, parts belligerently thicken where he had once been thin and taut. He heard his own voice at a friend's wedding breakfast toasting, "To Health." To health? Hadn't his carefree toast always been "To Love and Laughter?"

Then he met Jessica. And for the past four years he had been able to dismiss it all, the early morning stiffness, the shortness of breath on the tennis court, the wrinkles, the bulges. With her he felt insulated, safe from the assaults time was making on his body. But she was more than an elixir, a wrinkle eraser. In addition to quickening the pace of his heart, she filled him with a buoyancy of spirit, injected him with a lust different from the lust that came from savoring her body. Her youth, her enthusiasm, her passion. Indefinable, but it was there, a life force, an echo of himself.

He stood before the dresser searching for one of the blue-and-white-checked shirts she liked. He owned six of them. The tie he chose was less conventional than the ones he usually wore and he fashioned it into a slightly rakish knot. Still, in his own eyes, he looked out of sync, slapdash, pastiched. Never as together as her image of him.

Wallet, money clip, cigarettes, and lighter in their usual pockets, he turned to look at the bed. It was hard to believe that he and Sara had just left it after eight hours, so untouched, the sheets so smooth, still smelling of bleach and soap and sun. He closed his eyes, remembering the scent that used to fill this room.

He moved quickly down the stairs, checked the contents of his attaché case on the hall table. The house was still, the living room in perfect order, airless, dust-free. Even the ashes in the fireplace had been swept away. He straightened before pushing through the shuttered doors to the kitchen. Sara was at the stove, dressed in her robe. Handing him a mug of coffee, she offered her cheek for a kiss.

"I'll be late tonight, as usual," he said. "Do you have a class?"

"Not this evening. I'll be working on a paper in the library."

They sat at the breakfast table, the two of them, in the soft buttery light of a spring morning.

"You were very proud of her the other night," Sara said.

"Who?"

"Jessica Lenhart."

"She's the best producer I've got."

"Let's move back to the city, Ben. This house is so empty. We live in it like we barely exist."

"The city is a shooting gallery." He placed his hand on top of hers. "You miss the children, that's all."

"Yes, I do," she said, nodding her head. "But there's something else missing here."

In the hall, she helped him with his coat, handed him his attaché case. Standing at the open door, they embraced. "The city?" he said. "It's so serene here."

"We're too young for serenity."

He saw the pain in her morning eyes, the confusion in her tentative smile. He brushed his lips against her forehead. "We'll talk about it this weekend."

Walking the few steps to the garage, he noticed the basketball hoop that hung over the doors. The net was missing and thin streaks of rust stained the white shingles. He should have taken it down a long time ago. That was something else he would have to do this weekend. As he lifted the doors, he felt the warmth of the morning sun, the cold bite of the wind: a promise of spring with a reminder of the meanness of winter. That's the bitch about March, he thought, the meanness and the promise.

He liked living high above the city. Not that Doug's thoughts this morning were of lofty precepts of jurisprudence. When he saw Bambi curled up in an easy sleep, parts of him stirred with low-down lust. Last night he wanted to be all of himself. But with her he had come only fractionally closer. She was an aperture, and each time he felt as if he were screwing the starless night, spinning maddeningly off-center in a cosmic void. It was that impersonal.

Like his apartment, bought and paid for with his Wall Street salary before he went to work for Mel Shane. People were always surprised by the address and the size of the place. Somehow it didn't fit his rough-edged image. It was too neat, too much space for one man to fill. "It needs something," Wanda remarked when she first saw it. "A cat, a dog, a parrot, some life."

"What it needs," Mel replied, "is a woman."

There were women. But even in the bedroom, with its enormous bed, there was too much space to fill.

Bambi stirred and rolled over, her streaked blond hair tangled on the pillow. "You're awake," she said, stretching her arms toward him. And then with a pout of displeasure, added, "And dressed."

"Sorry," he said, "I've got to get to the office. Can you come back tonight? We could meet here and go out someplace to eat."

"I'm not sure. I may have to work."

"Let me know. You can leave a message at the office."

He walked the full length of the living room to draw the curtains. The glass doors to the small terrace rattled in the wind and in an instant he remembered another time, another terrace.

"It's much too cold to be standing out here, Doug," she said.

"Lee. My God. What are you doing at a party like this?"

"Drumming up business just like everyone else," she said. "It's been a long time, hasn't it? Let's have a drink."

Standing pressed against him at the crowded bar, she raised her glass. "Counselor."

"Counselor," he replied.

They had been in law school together, sitting in the same classrooms, studying in the same library, in competition with each other for the Journal. In a way their disadvantages made them equals. He was on scholarship and had to work nights; she was a woman. There was an attraction between them but their eyes were looking in different directions. Both made the Journal and both landed jobs with prestigious corporate law firms in New York. Only now, years after graduation, did they look at each other and make the connection that may have been there all along. They went home together that night and some time in the early morning hours, her head resting in the hollow between his arm and shoulder, she said, "I knew you were a good lawyer. I didn't know you were a magna cum laude lover."

They found an apartment and he discovered that living with Lee tested all of him, the quickness of his mind, the tenderness in his hands, the unrealized bounty in his heart. She sharpened parts of him that he was sure had been dulled by his parents' loveless marriage, by other women. She annihilated his fear of intimacy. And for the first time in his life he was exposed, defenseless, yet with her growing stronger every day. Minds and bodies locked together, they could share everything, he thought, the law, their lives, and because both had so much to prove, even their slightly cockeyed standards of success. They could have it all.

It began slowly, the unraveling. And at first he blamed himself. There was something she needed that he couldn't give her. Then he realized the one thing missing between them was time. She wanted to be with him only in intense ways, for intense moments. There was less time for prolonged moments of pleasure, for quiet times in between.

One night his passion for her filled him to the point of alarm. But he merely touched her, paused, and suddenly her eyes were fixed on him, impatient, judging. "Now," she said. "Here."

He felt like an adjunct, a clerk in her office. He called upon the hyperactive picture factory in his head to perform its usual magic. But it failed him and his passion ebbed.

"I see," she said, her hand searching.

That night they slept on opposite sides of the bed, an arid space between them. And in the morning it was forgotten. But he remained conscious of his failure, aware that she could not wait. There seemed to be time only for performance, no rehearsals to practice the lines and gestures that were new to both of them. He felt that he had been miscast, was wrong for the part she was asking him to play, and instead of reconstructing his role, he rebuilt the walls, stone by stone, that had crumbled at her feet.

"It isn't working, is it?" she said one evening when they both arrived home late.

"Do you have time to talk about it?" he asked.

"I don't deserve that."

"No, I'm sorry. It's only that I feel like I've lost an important case."

"We've both lost. I thought we wanted the same things. I thought we were so much alike. I love you, Doug."

"Not me," he said. "Someone you wanted me to be. We're very different, Lee."

"Then how do we do this, end it?"

"Like it began. Quickly. Honestly."

He moved out and the wound eventually healed. But ten years later, even though he thought the act of surgery had been forgotten, the tough, almost invisible scar tissue ached whenever he thought of her. She married someone else, got what she wanted. And left him with time for love, but no practice, no preparation. Room in his apartment, in his bed, only for Bambis.

He thought of Jessica Lenhart. Her ambition, her impatience were too familiar. She was not the sort of woman who would be diverted by the difficulty of his case. She had already been aroused by the intangible, seduced by the impossible. And if she were climactic, it would be on her terms. Now. Here. The only mystery was that half smile. What was behind it? Contempt for vulnerability, weakness, imperfection. What did she see through her camera's eye? He knew that his case could lead in only one direction: to a child who had been damaged by the drug. And when he finally found that child, would she ask him, smiling, to wave his stump of an arm, dance on his clubfoot, for her cameras? But was his way any better? Parading the child in a court of law, playing on the pity of a judge and jury?

Shuddering, he turned away from the terrace doors. And as he got ready to leave the apartment, he glanced into the bedroom. Bambi was curled up on his bed, watching television. He heard her light giggles over the mechanical sound of the laugh track. She did not see him. He did not say goodbye.

FIVE

*H*e sat behind the long, bleached oak table, his eyes searching for corroboration that all was in order within the serenity of his office. Beige couches and chairs, beige phones discreetly placed on low, angular tables, a beige wall covered with plaques and awards, a shiny altar of brass and silver dedicated to Lyman Ellis and his station. Everything cool, almost colorless, constructed in sleek, straight lines, with the exception of the exquisite, tortuously wrought Giacometti sculpture that stood on a pedestal near his desk. It was a gift from his wife Stacey.

Monica's voice on the intercom. "They're on their way up, Lyman."

Monica Albright had been with Lyman throughout his hopscotch travels around the corporate monopoly board. His graduation from Yale was followed by a brilliant career in the navy during the Pacific campaign. Then he joined the Defense Department where he held the post of Deputy Assistant for Congressional Affairs in the Eisenhower years. He moved to the Department of Commerce in the Kennedy years, then to the Eichendorn Foundation, and finally to American Power Resources where he served as liaison with the Defense Department that had spawned him. Now he had landed the job for which all his background and experience, his connections, his abilities and his slightly aesthetic appearance made him uniquely qualified: Chairman of the Board and chief executive officer of WPTN, the intellectual and cultural jackpot.

He couldn't have come so far so fast without Stacey. When they married twenty years ago, they had merged his talents with her money, his hunger for success with her wish to be a handmaiden to his ambition. And together they nursed his career and watched it grow, like the child they decided not to have.

Scott Mazden and Maureen Hahn breezed into his office. Scott wore, as always, a white suit, his imprimatur in a town where anonymity was a curse. Older and slightly taller than he was, an ivory cigarette holder poking from her fingertips, Maureen was dressed with the severe elegance that was her trademark. In charge of corporate fund raising and program development for the station, they had made themselves ubiquitous in the New York social scene, co-workers, compatriots in a crusade to find private dollars for public television, a rich benefactor to adopt their media orphan. Theirs was a business relationship, not a romance; neither had time or need for personal entanglements. They were themselves rather asexual. Their climaxes came only from the smell of power.

"We had to pass on the Emmys manqué, Lyman," Maureen said, leaning forward for a ceremonial kiss. "I don't see Jessica's plaque on your wall."

"Somehow the wall will survive without it."

Scott laughed the insincere laugh of a sycophant, like the member of the band who is obliged to laugh at the failing nightclub comic's jokes.

"Here's the revised fall lineup," Maureen said, handing Lyman a slender folder. "Still very tentative, I'm afraid. I think the BBC Kipling series will work on Thursdays."

"We're screening it for the oil people this week," Scott added. "I'm certain they'll agree to cover the major costs."

They sat around the low coffee table where Lyman conducted his business with office intimates. Scott smoothed the creases in his white suit and Maureen fitted a cigarette in her ivory holder as he glanced briefly through the folder. "Is this 'Aspects of Art' series old or new?" he asked.

"Completely new," Maureen said.

"What were the ratings on the last art series?"

"Not very impressive," Scott said. "But the critics liked it and our expenses would be minimal. It's a good buy, Lyman."

"I see you've rearranged Nevins's public affairs programming. Where are you putting his documentaries?"

"That's still up in the air," Maureen said. "It depends on how many of them we can afford to make."

"There I may have some good news," Scott said. "I think TML is on the hook. We've been after them for years without much luck. They've been spending their money on the commercial networks. But now it seems they're interested in selling their corporate image. And I think they're leaning in our direction instead of WNET's."

"That sounds promising," Lyman said. "Who have you spoken to there?"

"Someone called Arnold Sultan."

"Who's he?"

"Head of Public Information."

"TML," Lyman mused. "I know the man who runs it. Bradford Danziger. We met when I was in Washington. His predecessor patched together an enormous conglomerate— real estate, mining, some defense stuff. Danziger is making it work. Where do we stand at the moment?"

"I've shown Sultan the ratings, explained the financial picture. He seemed very knowledgeable about the tax side of it."

"Let me talk to Danziger," Lyman said.

"Of course." Scott removed an imaginary piece of lint from his snow-white suit.

"Maybe I can sell him on the idea of an unrestricted grant. He's in New York, isn't he? Stacey will arrange a dinner party. Of course, you're welcome to come, too, if you're free."

Their talk continued as Lyman examined the fall schedule, talk of gifts and grants, tax writeoffs and benefits. The tormented form of the Giacometti seemed to recoil from such a baffling combination of culture and commerce. When Scott and Maureen left, Lyman had time only to return to his desk and jot a name on his memo pad—Bradford Danziger—before Monica announced another visitor. "Ben Nevins," she said. "You don't have an appointment with him."

"That's all right, Monica. I can see him for a moment."

"This won't take long, Lyman," Ben said. "It's just a pro forma thing today. No noise, no lectures this time."

"That's all right, Ben. Please sit down." His gesture indicated a nearby chair, not the more intimate and comfortable furniture at the far end of his office. With Ben, he needed the distance, the authority, of a desk. "Now tell me what's on your mind."

"Jessica has come up with an idea for her next film. It's about a new drug just approved by the government that may be dangerous. She wants to look into how something like that could happen."

"I'm sure the drug company will be thrilled," Lyman sighed. "Why doesn't she stick to rats and roaches like the others?"

"I think she's interested in a different species of rodent," Ben said.

"What does the drug do that's so terrible?"

"Birth defects."

"I suppose that means showing the children. Would that be in good taste?"

"I don't know how tasteful it is," Ben said. "But it's part of the story."

Lyman rested his chin in the palm of his hand in a pose of thoughtfulness. "Yes, well all right. But I'm counting on you to keep an eye on her. You know Jessica tends to be . . . " he struggled for the right word, "excessive. Have you ever met any Saudis?"

"Only in Saudi Arabia," Ben replied, accustomed to such abrupt shifts in Lyman's conversation.

"Stacey and I are having some in for drinks this evening."

"Drinks? Drinks with Arabs?"

"I realize that. But Stacey spoke to some protocol people at State. Apparently they don't mind if drinks are served to the other guests. I was wondering what we're supposed to do about the women."

"Sorry, Lyman, can't help you there," Ben said, rising to leave. "And about that outburst last week. Maybe I went a little too far."

Lyman accepted apologies as graciously as he accepted compliments. "I've forgotten all about it," he said.

He hadn't forgotten at all. Ben pacing around his office after a budget meeting, his face flushed, his voice raised in anger. "Christ, Lyman, look at this lineup," he had barked. "Pretty little packages and not a goddamn thing in any one of them. This station is supposed to be free enough to snoop, to make trouble, tackle controversy, give people something to think about. The only new ideas we sell are for making quiche, the only snooping we do is in the bedroom of some horny old English king. It's boutique television!"

Lyman had heard it all before. How tired he was of Ben Nevins playing Don Quixote. Tired of Jessica Lenhart in her role as Mother Courage. And tired of the self-appointed media monitors who accused him of pandering to popular tastes, coddling corporations, using public television as his own private playpen. No one bothered to look at the figures. In only seven years he had built the station from nothing into a serious competitor for public support and prestige. He still had to beg for every dollar, but he did it with a top hat, not a tin cup. He had given the station stature, style.

There would always be critics to contend with, hands that had to be held. That was part of his job, and he had mastered it. There was only one problem that Lyman had never been able to solve. He was tall, but thin to the point of emaciation. As a child he had dreamed powerful dreams. As an adolescent he had prepared expectantly for the life of a man whose body would reflect his power. It never happened. And he never failed to notice the surprised expressions on the faces of people who knew him only by reputation, or through his deep resonant voice on the phone, when they found themselves looking at the spindly frame of Lyman Ellis.

Teratogenesis, teratology, teratosis. After combing through the card catalogue, she had spent most of the day in the stacks of the New York Public Library where she found dozens of articles in British and American medical journals and scribbled pages of notes: facts, statistics, dates, names, a crash course on the subject of teratogenic drugs, but only a very few references to Styralon. Then back to the catalogue, searching for information on FDA rules and regulations, procedures for new drug approvals, standards of safety and effectiveness. It was only a beginning, she knew, research, background, the jumbled pieces of a complex jigsaw puzzle with no picture on the box to tell her how to fit them all together. She was among the last to leave the library and there was only time enough for a quick trip back to the station to check her messages and find out what Ann had uncovered. And then to perform the Thursday afternoon ritual dance with Ben—the cursory good nights, see you tomorrow—before she returned to her apartment to await his arrival.

How had it happened? She had been working for him for more than a year, a year of hurried sandwiches in the station cafeteria, impersonal discussions of her films in his office or in the editing room. He was an exacting critic, asking the right questions, suggesting a different cut, a better reworking of her script, sometimes impatient, sometimes sarcastic, but his criticisms were always tempered with praise. And she was a quick study. His standards of excellence became her standards and she was grateful to him for the knowing and sensitive third eye he brought to her films. They were friends.

And as friends they began to lunch together in one or another of the little restaurants in the neighborhood of the station, trading anecdotes and ideas until the yawns and stares of the waiters hovering near their table drove them back to work. Slowly, they created a slender thread of intimacy—no more. It was only when Lyman Ellis intruded upon that relationship that they found themselves on the threshold of a much deeper affection.

Jessica's latest film on the increasing use of lie detectors as part of job interviews was in the can. And because Lyman had suffered some small embarrassment over an earlier film of hers, he came to the screening with a man from the legal department. A day or so later, in a combative mood, he called Ben and Jessica to his office and for half an hour, armed with legal memos, told them how the film had to be recut. Ben was outraged and the two men argued as if Jessica were not even in the room. When it was over and they were back in Ben's office, she was close to tears. "How can he do that, Ben?" she asked.

"He can't and he won't. Come on, Jess, let's get out of here. We both need a drink."

He missed his usual train back home and they had dinner together. Their first dinner. As they left the restaurant, his arm circled her waist and her arm found its way around the curve of his back. It was very natural, very quiet, combining the freshness of discovery with their familiar intimacy. For months they had shared words, touched in sentences, embraced in paragraphs. Now there were none. They walked in silence, each feeling the gentle pressure of the other's body, until he said, "Jess?" And her lips parted in a small circle as if to say, "Oh, I didn't know."

Because he had only a couple of hours before the last train, they went to one of the high-rise motor inns in that part of town, towering like a corrugated cardboard box over a foundation of garages and diners, shelter for tourists, conventioneers, and strangers wandering in off the street. Holding the door for her, he did not see her twist her small ruby ring around her finger so that it looked like a wedding band, a gesture wasted on the bored clerk at the reception desk. "For how long do you want it?" he asked through tight lips. Ben reached for the truth, discarded it, and said, "Just overnight."

They crossed a lobby decorated with pretensions of elegance: ugly orange brocade furniture squatting on dull brown nylon carpet. In the elevator, their senses were assaulted by canned music and the fetid odor of a cigar clamped in the mouth of a wiry gray-haired man with a tall redhead on his arm. Another man wore a shiny plastic badge pinned to his lapel that read: "Hi! My name is Bill." A couple clasped programs from a Broadway show that had been running for years. "One meets all of Paris here," Ben whispered.

Their room was a microcosm of the lobby, permeated by the stinging smell of disinfectant. In the bathroom, under harsh light, the white paper band stretched across the toilet seat promised standards of purity that were visible nowhere else. Ben threw his attaché case on a chair and dialed room service. "A bottle of Dom Perignon will transform this place into the Ritz," he said. Then, his eyes fixed on Jessica as if seeing her for the first time, he walked toward her and opened his arms.

"God, we can't stay here," he said. "I don't want to remember us in this place."

"There will be other nights, Ben. We can pretend it's the Ritz."

The champagne, an unknown domestic brand, was delivered in a styrofoam ice bucket and they drank it from plastic glasses. He turned off the lights and the room was filled with reflections from the blinking neon sign over the all-night garage across the street. He drew the curtains and was waiting for her in bed when she returned from the shower wrapped in a terrycloth towel. Looking at her with wonder, he pulled the towel away from her body and dropped it on the floor. She bent toward the night table, pretending to blow out candles.

And then the loving began. It was as if she were exposed film, an opaque, imageless strip lying in a clear solution, and he was the chemical elixir developing the flesh of her for the first time. Her mouth, her neck, the length of her forearms, her breasts, her thighs. With each touch, he transformed a dull negative into a vibrant form, an image so clear that it burst finally out of the fluid, more beautiful than she ever imagined she could be, more real than she had ever felt.

They lay on their backs, faces pressed together. "Jess, I bring you the best of me," he said. "All my years tell me that. You have the best part of me at the best time in my life. Do you understand?"

She understood. And it was she who reminded him of the time. He showered. They dressed together without saying a word and then clung to each other in a final embrace. "Ben, your watch," she said. He had left it on the night table.

The heavy summer night air hit them both as a startling reminder of reality. And just before she climbed into a cab, there was an awkward moment when they both realized they did not dare kiss. She turned to wave to him through the window but he was already striding toward the cab that would take him to the train.

The apprehension she felt the next morning when they met at the office evaporated instantly. His expression, the light in his eyes, reassured her that they had done it, crossed the boundaries of friendship into passion. And love seemed to follow almost as quickly. They did not dare have lunch together any more often than usual. But finding some excuse to take the last train home, he began coming to her apartment every Thursday night. And the days between Thursdays they shopped for presents, surprises. Once they met by accident in a department store and walked back to the station together, laughing, each carrying a large box that could not be given to the other for three days.

She came to love so much about him, that he was seasoned, had worked as a newspaper journalist, saw his own world in relation to larger realities. At work, without knowing it, she had been nourished by his experience. Now nothing in her life had meaning unless it first passed through the prism of his eyes. There were so many parts of him, even the part that had a wife and children. And she accepted that, as she accepted everything else about him. He never complained of his other life, whining, like some men, about the encroaching pain of their dry years as they sat with dewy young women in dimly lit restaurants. Only once had he said, "Why do I feel you know me, the ins and outs of me, better than anyone else?" It wasn't really true. She loved all of him, but she didn't know all of him, just as she could not have all of him. She did not question that, as she did not question the rightness of her love. She believed there was enough of him to share.

Her thoughts were not of the past or of the future. She was thinking of tonight as she returned to the station and rode the elevator up to her office. Ann was still there. "I was about to give up on you," she said. "What did you find?"

"Lots. Did you know that teratology is a medical specialty? There are doctors whose entire practice is the study of the causes of birth defects and how they can be treated. You should read some of this stuff. Statistics, graphs, charts. And they're writing about babies whose lives have been destroyed even before they're born."

"Did you happen to run across the name of Lionel Rudnick?" Ann asked.

"Of course. I've got some of his articles right here. How did you find out about him?"

Ann looked very smug. "Well, I've been doing a little digging, too. I called several obstetricians to find out what they knew about Styralon and birth defects. Not much on Styralon. One doctor remembered talking to a McCampbell salesman about it. But the one man who knows all there is to know about birth defects is Rudnick and he's right here at Columbia-Presbyterian. I spoke to his secretary and you have an appointment to see him Monday morning at ten o'clock."

"Annie, that's brilliant. God, what a ghoulish specialty. I wonder what the world's leading teratologist is like? Any messages? Any calls?"

"If you mean Doug Weber, no, not a word."

"Damn," Jessica said, slumping in her chair. "Well, we're not going to quit now. This is too important to wait around for a man with a problem."

In a futile attempt to bring some semblance of order to her small corner of the office, Ann began to tidy up her desk. "Come on, Jessie, let's get out of here. It's after six."

"No, you go ahead. Is Ben around? I've got to find him."

He found her. She recognized his knock, always a little impatient with closed doors. "You're back," he said. "Bad news, Jess. Let's take a walk."

Jessica followed him wordlessly down the hallway to the elevator. She almost had to run to keep up with him as he crossed the lobby and pushed his way through the revolving doors to the street. Only when they were half a block away from the station did he slacken his pace and take her arm. "I think I know what it is," Jessica said, trying to catch her breath, expecting the worst. "It's Lyman. He isn't buying Styralon."

"Hell, no, it isn't that," Ben said gruffly. "It's okay. You can do the story."

She felt her flesh tingle with excitement. "Ben, that's wonderful. Thank you. How did you do it?"

"Lyman's mind was somewhere else today. He's worried about serving martinis to some mullahs."

Rounding the corner, they had to separate to avoid bumping into a street vendor pushing his cart down the middle of the sidewalk. Then Ben took her arm again. "What is it?" Jessica said. "That's good news."

"There's been a fire in a chemical dump in Jersey. One of the crews is there and I have to handle this end of it for the eleven o'clock news. We can't have dinner, Jess. I can't leave the station."

It was not the fire, Jessica felt, but the felony that had just been committed. Time they stole had been stolen from them.

"Damn it, Jess. I won't be able to . . ."

"Ben, don't," she said. "It's happened before and we've survived. There will be other nights."

Across the street, even shabbier than they remembered it, they saw the corrugated cardboard motor inn where they had spent their first night together. "Remember the Ritz," he said, "we survived that, too, didn't we?"

"Survive? We flourish."

Nearing the station, their arms unlocked on a silent signal. The offices on their floor were empty and dark. Only the newsroom was pulsing with life. The wire service machines purred their familiar sound. Test patterns in muted shades of gray flickered on the monitor. "What have you got on the fire?" Ben shouted at one of the writers.

"I'm waiting to see the footage," he called back.

"Well, where the hell is it?"

"Biggest goddamn blaze I ever saw," another man said. "I just got back. The film's in the soup."

"Tell them to move it," Ben said. "I want to screen it now. A fire's a fire. I want people. Close-ups. Victims. And we need a survivor for the morning news."

Jessica returned to her own office. What kind of man was he? A man so tender that her whole body responded to his lightest touch. Yet she could still hear the dim echo of his voice in the newsroom demanding victims, survivors. Which was it? She did not know. She knew only that she wanted to be necessary to him, as he was to her. And like a guerrilla fighter she would have to inch toward that goal. It would take time to insinuate herself, infiltrate all the parts of him, so that she, too, would become indispensable. As indispensable as the attaché case that bounced lightly against her back whenever he stood in her doorway kissing her good night. But she was patient. Four years was not a long time. Terrorists did not understand such patience. Guerrilla lovers did.

SIX

She was not surprised at the ease with which Ann had obtained an appointment for her with Dr. Lionel Rudnick. In the past eminent scientists and authors had left their laboratories and typewriters, harried politicians had ducked out of urgent committee conferences, to meet her. An opportunity to be seen and heard on the massest of media was the lure. Her surprise came when she was directed to the pediatric wing of the sprawling Columbia-Presbyterian Hospital. She had expected to find him in some remote laboratory, studying complex genetic structures through an electron microscope. Dr. Rudnick dealt not only with the impersonal statistics that filled his scholarly papers. He was concerned with children.

He was a young man with pink cheeks and a thatch of strawblond hair, dressed in a business suit. No microscope, no white lab coat, no apothecary jars filled with mysterious specimens on dusty shelves. The walls of Dr. Rudnick's office were decorated with the colorful and impetuous splashes of children. "Miss Lenhart," he said, rising to greet her. "Please sit down. What can I do for you?"

"Thank you for seeing me on such short notice," she said. "With your permission, I'd like to take notes of our conversation."

"Of course," he replied. "What would you like to talk about?"

"Teratology. I've read some of your articles."

"Rather boring, aren't they?" Dr. Rudnick said cheerfully. "And most people who know of my work expect me to be a Dr. Frankenstein meddling around with the secrets of life."

Jessica laughed. "I'm not sure what I expected."

"Well, you see I'm not such a monster. Nor do I create them. And I'm grateful you have taken time to find out what I really do. That will spare you my lecture on the science of teratology."

"I'm not interested in teratology just as a science, Dr. Rudnick. I want to do a film on teratogenic drugs."

"Ah, thalidomide." He shook his head as if to say he should have known.

"No, that would be ancient history, wouldn't it?" Jessica said.

"Would it?" Dr. Rudnick's expression remained cherubic. "Which teratogenic drugs are you interested in? There are many in common use, you know."

"Many?" Jessica looked up from her notebook.

"Oh yes. Nicotine, alcohol, aspirin. It seems our society

cannot survive without them. But there are many other prescription drugs with known or suspected teratogenetic side effects that are truly necessary for survival. Some antibiotics, for example. There is, in the legal approval and use of any drug, what we doctors rather callously refer to as the 'risk versus benefit ratio.' Such a judgment call, however, is often very difficult to make."

"But with a teratogenic drug," Jessica said, "the birth of only a single deformed child would be too great a risk, wouldn't it? The drug would have to be banned."

"Even that's not quite so simple," Dr. Rudnick replied. "The birth of a single deformed child might not be considered 'statistically significant.' "

"Ten babies?" Jessica asked, her voice edged with sarcasm. "Twenty? A hundred? A thousand? Just when does a statistic become significant?"

"That, too," Dr. Rudnick said placidly, "must be a judgment call. Perhaps you do think I'm some kind of monster after all."

"I'm sorry, Dr. Rudnick. I didn't mean to imply . . ."

"Of course not. Any drug taken during pregnancy and even before, by *either* parent, I might add, must be prescribed with great caution. For years, teratologists lived in a fool's paradise, believing that the fetal barrier somehow protected the embryo in the womb. Now we know, the womb is not such a safe place after all."

"Is it possible that a new drug could be approved and prescribed in this country, even though there's some evidence that it's a teratogen?"

"It's possible."

"But how? After the horror of thalidomide?"

"I'm afraid that all thalidomide did was breed a healthy fear of thalidomide," Dr. Rudnick said, with a wry smile. "The FDA requires all new drugs to be tested for teratogenesis. But laboratory tests are sometimes inconclusive. And drugs prescribed during pregnancy cannot be tested clinically. What obstetrician, Miss Lenhart, would ask his patient to be a guinea pig? Unfortunately, the effects of teratogenesis are discovered only *after* the drug has been approved and prescribed. If the FDA is given all the facts, it does its job, most of the time. But I'm afraid I have very few kind words to say about the drug industry. Like automobile companies, they're in business to make money, not to save lives."

"Would a drug company deliberately withhold or falsify evidence to gain FDA approval?"

"If they do, it's at their own peril. But then they have the means and the will to defend their mistakes as aggressively as they sell their products. I've spent many hours in court testifying against them in birth defect cases. But don't get me started on my career as an expert witness. It takes up too much of my time as it is. Come, Miss Lenhart, I'd like to show you our laboratories and something of what we do here."

He guided her out of his office down a broad corridor. "I think you'll find our animal experiments fascinating," he said, and then added with his usual cherubic expression, "if you can forget, as I try to do, that what happens to them can also happen to children."

He pushed his way through double glass doors into a large room lined with hundreds of animal cages. Jessica caught her breath, overcome by the foul odor. Dr. Rudnick hung his suit coat on a hook by the doors and donned a long, white lab coat. "These are families of mice, Miss Lenhart. We use them because we know a great deal about their genetic system, which is very similar to our own. The experiments are quite elementary. We inject pregnant mice with various drugs and then kill them in progressive stages of their pregnancies to examine the litter for defects. Some of the mice die, of course, before giving birth. Others abort. Others we permit to give birth to monitor the mental and physical defects of their offspring."

He reached into a cage and held a tiny white mouse in the palm of his hand. It had stumps for paws, a misshapen mouth, half-closed eyes. Jessica was appalled by its deformities. Unable to look at the mutilated mouse, she pretended to take notes.

"It's necessary to do this, Miss Lenhart," Dr. Rudnick explained, returning the tiny animal to its cage. "The mother must be injected with a massive dose of the test drug. That's the only way we can determine its effects on the human embryo."

He led her through other glass doors to a small, brightly lit laboratory where a young man and woman wearing white jackets were bent over microscopes. "We conduct our more sophisticated experiments here," Dr. Rudnick said. "Perhaps they are beyond your scope of interest. But I'd like you to look at this." He pointed to a chart on the wall that showed the organs of the body lined up vertically in colored drawings: a blue brain, an orange eye, a green liver, yellow lungs, a red heart, and beside each organ was a number. "It's a rather oversimplified way of showing that the effect of a toxic insult on the fetus depends upon the time of development in which it acts. The first four to nine weeks of pregnancy are the most critical. Thalidomide affected the fetus at this time, and it affected ninety-five percent of those who took the drug. That's why it's called a 'hard' teratogen. But different toxic agents work at different times."

"And a drug prescribed to prevent miscarriage?" Jessica asked.

"The chances of miscarriage are greatest during the first nine weeks of pregnancy," Dr. Rudnick said. "If such a drug were teratogenic, every organ system in the body might show some degree of malformation."

"Even the heart?"

"Yes, even the heart. Teratogens injure the development of the heart, and exhausted, toxic blood bypasses the lungs and is pumped back into the body. Thus the heart becomes a conspirator of death, not life, in the newborn child. As tragic as it is, a child can live with deformed limbs, even distortions in sight, hearing, and brain function, but defects of the heart . . . Wouldn't you like to see some of our children, Miss Lenhart? They're quite remarkable. And they love to have visitors."

For a moment Jessica couldn't find her voice. Her throat felt dry. "I don't think so. Perhaps some other time."

"I understand," Dr. Rudnick said. He walked with her to the elevator. "And now, Miss Lenhart, before we say good-bye, may I ask you a question?"

"Of course."

"I assume you're interested in a specific drug, not in teratology as a specialty. May I ask which one?"

Jessica was caught by surprise. She had carefully phrased her questions to avoid any mention of Styralon. "I'm not at liberty to tell you that, Dr. Rudnick. I'm sorry. You have been very helpful to me."

"Ah well," he said, clasping her hand warmly, "perhaps I already know. If I can be of any further assistance, please call me. Your cameras would always be welcome here."

Her last view of Dr. Rudnick, as the elevator doors slowly closed, was his thatch of straw-blond hair and his smiling face.

"Sweet, but somehow a little sad," Jessica told Ann, back in the office. "The numbers are staggering and nobody pays much attention to what Dr. Rudnick does. Even I couldn't bear to look at the children. God, Annie, what's the matter with me? I've filmed starving kids, battered kids, kids working in factories and migrant camps. I hate this film already. Maybe Doug Weber will say no."

"And maybe not," Ann said. "He called."

"And?"

"Well, his voice is very sexy over the phone, deep, intense. He can't be all bad."

"Damn it, Annie, what did he say?"

"He didn't sound too thrilled about it, Jessie, but he says okay, you can do the film. He's sending over some information about the labs that tested Styralon. But you're not supposed to do anything without consulting him first. And another item of interest. Miss Jessica Lenhart, the distinguished award-winning filmmaker for public television, has an appointment with the public relations department of McCampbell Pharmaceuticals in Maplewood, New Jersey. I told them you might bring a film technician with you, just in case Doug Weber wants to tag along."

"Not on this trip," Jessica said. "And if he finds out about it, we're dead."

"This is ready for you to sign," Ann said, handing Jessica an office form.

She read it quickly. "Budget Requisition Form 408. Producer: Lenhart, Title: Styralon, Air date: July 21, Budget number—" She scrawled her signature at the bottom of the page. "Fine, but there's one thing. Let's keep Styralon out of it."

"Of course. That was dumb of me. What do you want to call it?"

Jessica thought for a moment and again, this time in her memory, she saw Dr. Rudnick's cheerful smile. "Just for now," she said, "let's call it 'Defects of the Heart.' "

SEVEN

*T*he pale-green and white sign, rising from a nest of ever-greens, was discreet, tasteful: MCCAMPBELL PHARMACEUTICALS. Ducks paddled about in a small pond in front of a low modern structure that fit the contours of the landscape. In the lobby, water bubbled through a pool carved out of the same green and white marble that paved the floors. In the center of the pool was a statue: Gregory A. McCampbell, founder. Again, green and white marble. Jessica got it. Green and white: McCampbell's team colors.

She identified herself to the uniformed security guard and a few moments later heard the sharp click of heels across the marble floor. Helen Lassiter, director of public relations for McCampbell Pharmaceuticals, was dressed in a gray tailored suit with a ruffled white blouse peeking out at the neck. Her pale pink lipstick matched her pale pink fingertips, in premeditated coordination. "Miss Lenhart. Welcome to McCampbell."

"You were very kind to invite me," Jessica said.

"It's an extraordinary building, isn't it?" Mrs. Lassiter said. "Our guided tours have become very popular with the public. Come, let me show you around."

She conducted her tour with a well-rehearsed line of patter. "We moved here just four years ago from Union City. Our manufacturing facilities are still located there. It's a pity you've come now. In just a few weeks, there will be flowers everywhere."

Mrs. Lassiter's office was as carefully designed as she was, combining both masculine and feminine motifs in a spectrum of yellows with a few loyal touches of green and white. "May I get you some coffee, tea?" she asked, one finger poised on the intercom button of her phone. "No? Then what may we do to help you?"

Jessica had her pitch prepared. "I have to be frank with you, Mrs. Lassiter. My assistant may have given you the impression that I want to make a film about McCampbell. That's not quite the case. I'm making a documentary about the American drug industry as a whole, both as a multi-million-dollar business and as a major force in our lives. McCampbell is only one of the companies I plan to include."

"I understand, Miss Lenhart. Thank you for your candor. But isn't that a rather large order? There are hundreds of companies manufacturing thousands of drugs in this country. Wouldn't it be easier to focus on just one or two?"

"I've thought of that," Jessica said. "But those companies would have to be typical of the entire industry."

"We here at McCampbell don't think of ourselves as typical. We are extraordinary in every phase of our operations. Perhaps you'd like to look at these when you have time. This is our annual report and this is our company history published just last year. And may I make another suggestion?"

"Of course."

"I've had a great deal of experience with filmmakers. Part of my job entails working with the very talented people who specialize in making industrial films which are, in my opinion, a neglected art form. I've also worked on the films we use to promote our products at medical conventions and the like. And I've found that films have their greatest impact when they deal with a single subject—*in depth.*"

"You mean focus on a single company?"

"Yes. And if you decided on McCampbell, our extensive film library would be available to you. That would certainly save you a great deal of work."

"I'd have to think about that, Mrs. Lassiter. It might be interesting, but where's the hook, something to hang it on? A personality, or maybe even one of your products."

"That's a marvelous idea," Mrs. Lassiter exclaimed.

"No, on second thought, I can't do that. We might be accused of plugging a product."

"But wouldn't that depend entirely on the product? If, for example, McCampbell had pioneered a new drug certain to be hailed as a medical miracle, your film would be a public service. You might trace the history of that drug, from its invention through every phase of the process that finally makes it available to the American people. What better way to show how a drug company operates? From the specific to the general. Another time-tested film technique."

"Yes, something like that might work," Jessica said cautiously. "Do you have a drug in mind?"

"McCampbell has many remarkable drugs. But wait

a minute. There's one that would be absolutely perfect."

Jessica leaned forward expectantly. Would she, could she possibly have such good luck?

"Intrafetamyecin," Mrs. Lassiter said proudly.

"That's an interesting name." Jessica hoped her disappointment was not apparent. "What does it do?"

"It's the breakthrough medical researchers have been seeking for years to arrest Grimaud's Syndrome."

"How exciting. But isn't that rather obscure? There must be another drug just as dramatic, something the average person would understand and care about because it affects his everyday life?"

Helen Lassiter's face clouded. "Well, there is one we're all very proud of. Anthrodorphin."

"Anthrodorphin," Jessica repeated somewhat incredulously. "And what does that do?"

"It's extremely effective against a powerful new strain of gonorrhea," Mrs. Lassiter said rather apologetically. "I suppose a lot of people would be interested in that."

"I'm sure they would be, but I don't think my station would be too happy about an hour on the subject of venereal disease. You must have something more wholesome."

"Well, let me see. Something dramatic, something wholesome . . . Of course! Why didn't I think of it before. This one really is perfect. A new drug ready to go on the market. And it *is* a medical miracle."

"What's this one called?" Jessica asked apprehensively.

"Styralon."

"How do you spell that?" Jessica bent her head over her notebook to conceal a smile.

"S-t-y-r-a-l-o-n." Mrs. Lassiter articulated each letter carefully.

"And what's it for?"

Mrs. Lassiter spoke with enthusiasm. "It prevents miscarriages, Miss Lenhart. For millions of women, a miscarriage, whatever its cause, is the greatest tragedy in their lives. And for millions more, the fear of miscarriage can turn their pregnancies, months that should be spent in blissful anticipation, into a nightmare. Styralon will banish all those worries. The woman's angle, Miss Lenhart. I don't have to remind you how important that would be to your film."

"And this is a new drug?" Jessica asked.

"Yes, the testing was completed a year ago, we have FDA approval and we're now in the process of marketing it."

"Oh," Jessica said with a small frown of disappointment. "If it's that far along, what is there for me to film? Perhaps there's another drug at an earlier stage . . . "

"I'm surprised at you, Miss Lenhart. If you began with a drug that was still in its research and development phase, your film would take years to make, and would be as long as Gone With the Wind. Styralon is a fait accompli and you would have a built-in happy ending, also important for your film."

"Happy ending?"

"The millions of babies' lives it will save. We could recreate the early history of the drug for your cameras. We do it all the time for our own films."

"It just might work," Jessica said thoughtfully. "What a joy to talk to someone who knows so much about films."

"It's all part of my job," Mrs. Lassiter said airily. "Now, why don't you come with me and I'll show you how you could film most of the Styralon story right here. 'The Styralon Story,' " she exclaimed. "What a marvelous title!"

Their journey took them along thickly carpeted corridors and through a glass-enclosed tunnel that provided a fractured view of McCampbell's bucolic setting. "This is the south wing, our Research and Development facility," Mrs. Lassiter explained, and Jessica saw before her an expansive laboratory in which at least forty people were at work. She remembered Dr. Rudnick and the two lone medical students in his cramped and antiquated laboratory at Columbia-Presbyterian. "Would you be able to arrange an interview with the person who led the Styralon research here?"

"Of course. Dr. Alton Medford, the chief of R&D and, I must say, a very photogenic man."

"Does McCampbell conduct animal research?" Jessica asked.

Mrs. Lassiter's face assumed a grave expression. "Yes, it's absolutely essential, in spite of what the animal lobby says. The labs are below us in the basement. But we don't include them on our guided tour, and I don't imagine your viewers would want to see them either."

As they passed through another glass-enclosed tunnel to a different wing of the building, Mrs. Lassiter said, "As you may not know, the government requires even further testing by independent laboratories, and Styralon passed through that phase with flying colors."

"Is there someone I might interview who was connected with that?"

Mrs. Lassiter thought for a moment. "Well, yes. Karl Engle at Chanterelle Laboratories in Garden City, Long Island. They've done a great deal of work for us in the past. And Dr. Engle is a very interesting man. What he does is rather plodding and meticulous. Nothing quite as dramatic as what we do here. And his labs are not nearly as attractive as ours. But I'm sure he would be happy to talk to you."

"And what about government approval?" Jessica asked.

"How could I forget that? The FDA is a typical bureaucracy, I'm afraid. The approval process seems to take forever and it's the consumer who suffers. Fortunately, Styralon was approved without much delay. But I don't know how you could film the FDA. Your viewers would be bored to death."

Mrs. Lassiter ushered Jessica down another carpeted corridor. "Do you know where you are now?" she asked. "Right back where we started. My office is over there. But this is what I want you to see."

Smiles and waves greeted Mrs. Lassiter as she showed Jessica through McCampbell's Division of Public Information. "What we do here," she said, "is just as scientific as the work in R&D. Once a new drug has been approved, it must be made available to the public. Our department for professional education reaches the doctors who will prescribe the drug and the pharmacists who sell it; our department of consumer education reaches the patients who will benefit by it. Advertising, publicity, my own public relations department, the art department—it's a very complex business. Then there's the Sales and Marketing Division, the men who actually call on doctors and pharmacists in the field with samples of our products. McCampbell's sales and marketing techniques have set the standard for the entire drug industry."

"Who's the director?" Jessica asked.

"Mr. Herbert Shannon."

"Would he consent to be interviewed?"

"Herb? He'd be delighted. He's such a ham. Now here's something I'd like to show you. The pamphlet we'll be sending out nationwide on Styralon."

Jessica examined the glossy folder. The name STYRALON was spelled out on the cover in white letters on a deep blue background like fluffy clouds floating across the sky. Inside, under the headline: "A Trouble-free Pregnancy Thanks to Styralon," there were pictures of radiant pregnant women in tennis clothes, jogging outfits, dancing, bicycling. And on the back cover, a mother gazing serenely at a fat, healthy, raspberry-cheeked baby cradled in her arms. "May I keep this?" Jessica asked.

"Of course."

Seated again in her office, Mrs. Lassiter said, "There you have it, Miss Lenhart. The Styralon Story from start to finish."

"You've given me so much to think about," Jessica said. "But there's one more thing: the people who run your company. Will they let me make a film on Styralon?"

"I see your point. The Styralon Story was really a sort of spur-of-the-moment inspiration, wasn't it? I would have to speak with my superiors, but I think I can assure you of our complete cooperation."

"And, of course, I'll have to check with mine," Jessica said.

"Then, why don't we leave it this way, Miss Lenhart? Phone me when you have your go-ahead, and McCampbell Pharmaceuticals will play its part, I promise you. Perhaps the next time I see you, you'll be here with your cameras."

"I hope so."

Helen Lassiter said goodbye to Jessica in the green and white marble foyer. "I'm sorry you can't stay for lunch," she said. "The lobster in our company dining room is delicious."

"Perhaps next time." Jessica was standing at the pool with its bubbling water. "There is one more question I'd like to ask," she said. "And please don't be offended, but has McCampbell ever marketed a product that gave cause for legal action against the company?"

"I'm not offended at all," Mrs. Lassiter assured her. "It's inevitable, whenever you are serving the public. Your television station has a legal department, I'm sure. There have been suits against our company because of some completely unexpected side effects that could not have been predicted even after the most exhaustive testing. But our legal department is primarily concerned with contracts and patents."

"And Styralon," Jessica said. "Is it possible that it might cause some unexpected side effects?"

"The drug is designed for use by pregnant women, Miss Lenhart. It has been approved by the government. Such a suggestion is monstrous."

From the window of the bus heading toward New York, she watched the bright blue skies of suburban New Jersey fade into the purplish-yellow color of a bruise. There were no ducks, no flowers in that bleak industrial landscape. But somewhere there was another McCampbell sign, another part of the company's operation: the factory that manufactured its chemicals and the assembly lines that turned out millions of pills and capsules. Leafing through the annual report Mrs. Lassiter had given her, Jessica saw that McCampbell's profits were also in the millions. Money and power.

The bus swerved into the toll plaza of the Lincoln Tunnel and the Styralon brochure resting on her lap slid to the floor. When she leaned to pick it up, she saw once more the raspberry-cheeked baby, the Madonna-like smile of the mother, and her filmmaker's sense began working instantly. The camera on the animation stand would slowly zoom in on the picture of the baby, with the voice of Dr. Lionel Rudnick saying, "As tragic as it is, a child can live with deformed limbs . . . " She would dissolve through the baby to a medium shot of the mouse in Dr. Rudnick's hands. "But defects of the heart . . . " he would say, as she panned over to him, losing the mouse, pushing in for an extreme close-up when he returned the animal to its cage.

Then she would dissolve again. To what? Dr. Karl Engle, Chanterelle Laboratories. It would be a match dissolve, mouse to mouse. In Dr. Engle's laboratory, she knew, the mouse would not be deformed.

 *EIGHT*

*T*he crew car was inching slowly through the crush of late afternoon traffic on the Long Island Expressway. The three men sat crowded together in the front seat. Jessica was alone in the back where at least she didn't have to look at their faces as they embarked on their favorite topic of conversation.

Dan Spignole was saying, "So I told her, Irene, you never know what'll happen tomorrow. You've got to live each night as it comes. How can you live today always thinking about tomorrow?"

"You're a true existentialist, Spignole," Jack Everett said. "Ever read Camus?"

"Do you know which exit, Jess?" Tom Whiteside asked over his shoulder.

"*I* know," Spignole said. "Don't bother the lady. She's reading. So I told this broad, we come to Chicago a lot. You've got to give them that. Because no matter what you say, they always think about tomorrow. Anyway, she's built like a . . . "

It had begun, the inevitable tales of their extramarital triumphs with the nameless, faceless women they picked up at restaurants and bars as they made their way from one film to another, turning motel rooms into palaces of pleasure where, for fleeting moments, they could forget the tedium of their lives. Spignole, the cameraman, always led it off, but Whiteside, the soundman, and even Everett, the young assistant cameraman who still retained a few ideals about his craft, would soon be drawn into this morass of sexual one-upsmanship.

Jessica had endured these conversations before, these neutered moments, listening to them speak as if she were a lifeless heap in the back seat. It was worse than the brusque, surly way they often treated her when they were filming an interview, worse than the bad lighting, the out-of-focus footage. Working, they at least acknowledged her existence. At times like this, she was sexless, invisible.

She shut out their voices and began reading Ann's memo.

Fact: The FDA approves some 400 new drugs every year. Busy place.

Fact: Chanterelle is just one of more than fifty labs in the U.S. that perform tests for drug companies. It's big business. In some cases of testing abuses in the past, it has been proved that the lab had stock or some other sort of financial connection with the drug company. And do you know that McCampbell is only one of a whole slew of companies owned by a New

York–based conglomerate? I picked that up in their annual report. Mega-
bucks, Jessie, megabucks.

Fact: When alarming findings on new drugs are discovered either by
the lab or the independent physicians who also perform tests, by statute
they are supposed to be reported to the FDA. Lots of luck! In my research,
I've turned up at least twenty cases in which drug companies have sheltered
the government from such unpleasant information. With Styralon, that
means either Chanterelle or McCampbell, or both, may be sitting on
unfavorable reports. The plot thickens.

Fact: The Academy of Medicine is a goldmine of information about
Styralon. It was, believe it or not, hailed by the English medical establish-
ment as the greatest thing since penicillin. The few doctors who started
blowing whistles were ignored, but the whistles are growing louder. As
far as I can tell, they're still writing about lab experiments in all the
articles, not babies. No definite link there yet.

Fact: Karl Engle has been director of Chanterelle research for five years,
been with the lab for fifteen. Two more phone calls from him yesterday
afternoon wanting to know if he should wear a blue shirt and if he would
have to be made up. Obviously excited about the interview, which is a
switch from his cool, sniffy response to our initial inquiries. I figure he
checked with McCampbell and got a go-ahead.

Fact: Doug Weber is a very touchy man. Couldn't understand how you
arranged an interview with Engle so fast. Wanted to know why he wasn't
informed, why you didn't ask him to go with you, etc., etc. Demands
to see the interview as soon as it's ready to screen. A royal pain, but I
still think he has a sexy voice.

"That's it, for Christ's sake. Pull in," Spignole barked.
"Didn't you see the sign? How about some exteriors, Jess?
If you want my opinion, Chanterelle Labs looks like a shoe
factory."

"Maybe on the way out," Jessica said. "I'll be asking some
tricky questions, Dan, so keep the film rolling, no matter
what he says."

Jack Everett, who also retained a few civilities along with his idealism, opened the car door for her. "Make sure the slate is right, Jack," she said.

"Okay, lady," Spignole said, loading Everett with as much camera equipment as he could carry. "Day One. Roll One. Picture and Sound. Let's make a movie."

While the crew set up the camera and lights in his office, Jessica chatted amiably with Dr. Karl Engle. He was a tall, heavyset man, probably in his mid-fifties, with a bald head and a face covered with a thick bushy beard. "We knew Styralon was a remarkable drug when we began work on it," he said. "We expected articles in the professional journals, perhaps something in *Time* or *Newsweek,* but we never thought it would be the subject of a film."

"Okay, Jess," Everett said, motioning them into the office. "We're ready."

"Sorry, Doc," Spignole said, clapping Karl Engle on the back. "We had to move things around for a better angle."

"That's quite all right," Dr. Engle replied agreeably. "I'm afraid my office is not very large. Most of our space is devoted to our laboratories."

"Your office is fine," Jessica said. "Now if you'll sit behind your desk, Dr. Engle, I'll be right over here, next to Dan. But please, look into the camera, not at me, when you answer my questions."

The light stands set up in a small semicircle around his desk bathed Dr. Engle in a harsh white glare. He stroked his beard and pursed his lips nervously as Tom Whiteside pinned a microphone to the lapel of his jacket.

"Roll One, Picture and Sound, Profile of a Miracle, Dr. Engle, Take One." Jack Everett snapped the wooden slate and walked quickly out of camera range. "Speed, Jess.

You've got speed," he said, his eyes intent on the small counter behind Spignole's camera.

"Thank you for letting us see you today, Dr. Engle," Jessica began. "We're doing, as I told you, a film on the pharmaceutical industry. And we're interested in showing how a miracle drug like Styralon came into being. I understand you know a good deal about it." Her arms clasped around her knees, she spoke to him from her position on the floor just to the right of the camera.

"Indeed I do," Dr. Engle said. "You see, my laboratory, that is Chanterelle, was asked by the drug company that pioneered Styralon to do the initial testing required by the government."

"Have you done research for McCampbell in the past?"

"Yes, we have a long and pleasant association with McCampbell. It's a fine company."

"I think most people would assume that a drug company performs its own tests on a new drug."

"That would be impossible." Dr. Engle's tone was indulgent. "No drug company has the personnel, the equipment, or the resources to carry out such a long and laborious procedure."

"Oh, I see," Jessica said, knowing that the law required independent tests. "Would you explain your position at Chanterelle?"

"I'm the director of research."

"And on Styralon?"

"I supervised the research on Styralon." His voice grew more confident.

"What percentage of your laboratory's business would you say comes from McCampbell?"

Dr. Engle stirred slightly and stroked his beard. "I really have no idea."

"And what's the nature of the financial relationship between your laboratory and McCampbell?"

"We are paid for our services. Is that what you mean?"

"I understand that. But if, for example, a laboratory gave an unfavorable report on a drug to the company that manufactures it, would it risk losing future jobs for that company?"

"Chanterelle has submitted many unfavorable reports," Dr. Engle said, turning from the camera to look at Jessica. "I find that question highly improper. And what does that have to do with Styralon?"

"Nothing. You're right, Dr. Engle. Let's talk about Styralon." She made a circular motion with her fist, signaling Spignole to move in for a closer shot. "Just what was involved in your tests and how long did they take?"

Dr. Engle relaxed. "Let me say only that our tests were exhaustive. McCampbell and the FDA would be satisfied with nothing less."

"And the results?"

"Completely satisfactory. Thanks largely to our work, Styralon was ruled both safe and effective for its intended purpose: the prevention of miscarriage. And if I may say so, I'm proud that I took part in the development of a drug that will be of such great benefit to the world."

"To your knowledge, then, Styralon has no unpleasant side effects?"

"Only the usual ones that can come with any drug, Miss Lenhart. Temporary changes in blood pressure, drowsiness, some nausea. In biology as in physics, every action has a reaction."

"Please try not to call me by name when you answer my questions, Dr. Engle. I won't be appearing in the film. And try to look into the camera." She circled her fist again for an extreme close-up. "Was there any evidence that Styralon is a teratogen?"

Dr. Engle drew back with visible alarm. "Stop the camera," he said angrily, holding his hand in front of his face. He got up, pulled off the lapel mike, and strode away from his desk. "Now see here, Miss Lenhart. I find your whole line of questioning outrageous. First you insult my integrity and then you imply that Styralon is a dangerous drug. You've misrepresented your motives in coming here."

Jessica signaled Spignole to stop filming. Then getting to her feet, she moved to the shadowy corner of the office where Dr. Engle stood, his face flushed and angry. "I apologize, Dr. Engle. But don't you see, I'm only asking the questions you must have asked the people under you who tested the drug. And if your wife were pregnant, wouldn't she ask her doctor the same question: 'Will it hurt my baby?' I only used the word 'teratogen' because I know the government requires such tests. I don't think the average viewer would even know what it means."

"I can't see what possible good it would do to alarm people with suspicions. Even asking the question in your film is irresponsible, Miss Lenhart. I'm not sure I care to continue the interview."

"That's entirely up to you," Jessica said. "You're a scientist who specializes in objective inquiry, Dr. Engle. So do I. I didn't mean to offend you. Please. The Styralon story won't be complete without you."

Dr. Engle stroked his beard. "Well, all right. There are one or two more things I'd like to say."

"You got speed, Jess," Everett called out. "Profile of a Miracle, Dr. Engle, Take Two." And the snap of the slate.

Back at his desk, the lapel mike in place, Dr. Engle began deliberately: "At any given time, several drugs may be undergoing tests here at Chanterelle. I supervise all of them, but you must understand that I do not personally conduct the tests myself."

"Was that the case with Styralon?" Jessica asked.

"Yes. The man responsible for the Styralon tests was Dr. Daniel Bowen."

"Would Dr. Bowen consent to answer a few questions for us while we're here?"

"Dr. Bowen is no longer employed by Chanterelle. He has retired."

"I see," Jessica said. "Just what was the nature of his work?"

"Dr. Bowen collated reports from our own technicians and other sources, gathered statistics from the biologists who conducted the animal tests. Nothing glamorous, but the kind of work Daniel Bowen was suited for. Many long hours of staring at embryonic formations on slides, writing papers on cellular reconstruction, studying pathology reports. Blood pressure studies, hematology studies. Even if you were to talk with him, you would find most of what he had to say completely incomprehensible."

"Could Dr. Bowen's reports be made available to me?"

"The reports submitted to the government are available to anyone, Miss Lenhart. But others remain the confidential property of McCampbell."

"Do you know where Dr. Bowen is now?"

"I have no idea. He could be anywhere. He's a rather odd man, you know."

"Odd? In what way."

"Moody, very emotional, sometimes indiscreet. A genius in his own way, I suppose, but he's an old man who has spent his entire life peering into microscopes and maybe that's to be expected. I'm sure there's nothing he could tell you that would add to what I've had to say."

"You're probably right, Dr. Engle, even if we knew where he was. A few more questions and then we'll be finished."

Jeff Russell stopped the Moviola, freezing the frame on Karl Engle's bearded face. "Look at the glare on his head, and the hair in the gate. Christ, Jess, doesn't Spignole check the lens?"

Jeff's eyes were blood red and bleary. He wore a look of chronic exhaustion that came not from overwork or boozy nights. It was the minor things of his life—braces for his daughter, his car's dying engine, the mortgage on his house —that wore him down. But in spite of his sharp tongue and red-rimmed eyes, Jessica knew he was a man of endless energy and enormous talent.

"Can't you have it scrubbed in the lab?" she asked.

"I can try." He rewound the soundtrack and reached for a white marking pencil to remind himself of the scratch on the negative.

Doug Weber was sitting on a small stool in the darkened editing room, blinking at the tiny screen of the Moviola. "Not bad. Not bad at all," he said. "I liked Engle's reaction when you mentioned the word 'teratogen.' How did you get him to go back on camera?"

"Charm, pure charm," Jessica said. "And then he began passing the buck to Daniel Bowen. Have you ever heard that name?"

"No, that's a new one."

"I'll have Ann check the medical directories. I'd like to interview him even if he is retired."

"Maybe he didn't retire," Doug said.

Jeff reached for the overhead light to darken the room. "This is slated Four, the last roll," he said. Then they heard the sound of Jessica's off-camera voice and once again the face of Karl Engle appeared on the Moviola screen.

"You are, of course, familiar with the interrelationship between government and industry in testing and approving new drugs, Dr. Engle. In your opinion, is it an effective system?"

"It's the best we've got," Dr. Engle replied crisply. "Not perfect, perhaps, but then it's always easy to criticize the system. Private industry and the government are not adversaries, you know. They must work together to serve the public. In the pharmaceutical industry, we welcome government supervision. But we are only human, after all. In any business, you'll find some men who are victims of their own egos, prisoners of their past triumphs, or touched by some personal tragedy that renders them useless. And there are those whose lack of vision can threaten the success of an entire project. But they are the exceptions. No, I don't criticize the system. That can incapacitate you, stop you from doing the work that must be done. As for Styralon, it's a good drug. It will help people, and that, it seems to me, is much more important than philosophical speculations about the system."

"Thank you, Dr. Engle, for your time . . . "

The last image of Karl Engle flickered and disappeared, leaving the Moviola screen filled only with a yellow-white blankness.

"Beautiful," Doug said. "Remember I told you that I couldn't sue a system? Well, maybe I can't, but you just filmed it."

"Yeah," Jeff cracked as he placed Mylar tape on the flapping end of the roll of film and turned up the lights in the editing room. "Sounds to me like the good doctor's got a case of integritus interruptus. Come on, let's get a cup of coffee in the cafeteria."

"I'll meet you there," Jessica said. "I have to go to my office. There's something I want to show you, Doug."

Jeff and Doug walked through the corridors that led to the cafeteria, brushing past the cleaning women who were pushing carts loaded with brooms and mops. An old man was dragging plastic containers filled with garbage from the cafeteria toward the freight elevator. "So now what do you think of the glamour of television?" Jeff asked. "Promise you won't tell my mother what it's really like."

They picked up damp trays from the rack and waited patiently for the yawning waitress to pour their coffee. "You ever see Jess's office?" Jeff said. "That's another revelation."

"No, this is the first time we've worked together."

"So she tells me. And I gather you weren't too crazy about the idea. But don't worry, you're both in the same business."

"What's that?"

"Changing the world. I'll tell you a very poorly kept secret around here. She's a little like Alice in Wonderland. Falls down head first into some gaping hole, somehow lands on her feet, and then starts asking questions. Nothing fazes her. Look at the way she handled Engle. Any other producer would have lost him. Still, I sometimes think she gets too involved. But things have to make sense to Jess, and if they don't, she has to find out why. Like Alice."

"You've worked with her before," Doug said.

"Ever since she made her first film. She's the best. The others are paying the rent. She cares. Sometimes too much."

They saw her enter the cafeteria, file folders tucked under her arm. She got a cup of coffee and joined them at their table.

"I was just telling your friend here," Jeff said, "that you make great movies."

"Thanks, but I think I'd prefer your usual crusty criticism."

"Crust, I'll give you crust. This nice guy hands us a great story and we bring him here?"

"He doesn't approve of expense accounts," Jessica said.

"Live and learn, buddy," Jeff said. "I've got to go back and take a look at Seiden's latest, Jess. Ghetto life through the eyes of a child. Cutest goddamn little black kid you ever saw. I don't know where he finds them. Nice meeting you, Counselor. Enjoy." And he left them with his usual world-weary walk.

"Who's Seiden?"

"Another producer here. He has a rather rosy view of life."

"Jeff says you're the best. Calls you Alice in Wonderland."

"I couldn't do it without him. And if I'm Alice, he's the March Hare. Ours is a unique relationship." She opened one of the file folders she had brought with her. "This is what I wanted you to see."

"I liked the way you handled Engle," Doug said. "I'm sorry I gave your assistant such a hard time about the interview. She sounds like a nice girl."

"She's a very grown-up woman of twenty-two. And she's used to hard times. After all, she works with me. And by the way, why did you decide to let me make this film? After our lunch I thought I'd never see you again. What changed your mind? Was it Mel?"

Doug leaned back in his chair, clasping his hands behind his neck in the posture that was becoming very familiar to her. "He applied a little pressure, but it was my decision. And I'm still not sure it was the right one. Your film could put me in a very tricky legal position. But we're after the same thing, or at least I think we are. We just have different methods, that's all."

"And your case. Where does it stand?"

"Still nothing here. But I'm in touch now with the group of lawyers and doctors in England who are trying to stop

Styralon over there. They've found children with birth defects they suspect were caused by the drug. But they haven't been able to prove a positive connection."

"We have to find a victim," Jessica said.

"But I've got time. You're the one with an air date."

"And you're afraid my obligation to make it will screw up your case?"

"Can you assure me it won't?"

"No, I can't. Can you assure me that every day that passes isn't closer to the day some pregnant woman in this country will take that drug? Neither of us has time, Doug."

"But your business lives on time. Devours it. Promise me you'll be careful, keep me informed."

"I will, I will," she sighed. She still had not told him about her trip to McCampbell, but how he exhausted her with his need for promises. And what could he promise in return? If her business lived on time, his profession killed it.

"What's your next move?" he asked.

"We've got to find Daniel Bowen. From the look in Karl Engle's eyes, I suspect you're right. He didn't retire at all. I think he was fired."

"Or paid off."

"That's possible, too. Obviously, Chanterelle and McCampbell have something to hide. If Dr. Bowen agrees to talk, I've got a film."

"And I've got a witness. But where is he?"

"Maybe we'll find out in Washington." She handed Doug some papers from the folder. "These are my letters to Kenneth M. Herrelson. He's in the Office of New Drug Evaluation. I have a date with him next Tuesday in his office. Do you want to come along?"

"You're damn right I do," Doug said. "How did you get to him? They've been stonewalling me."

"I just called up and asked to talk to the person who knew

the most about recently approved drugs. I got bounced around until I got Herrelson and told him I was doing a film on Styralon."

"Mel was right," Doug said, shaking his head. "You're incredible."

"Maybe not. Herrelson won't talk on camera. All I could get was an interview. And from my past experience with Washington bureaucrats, I don't think he'll tell us very much. But Madge Barwick may be another matter."

"Whoa, slow down. Who's Madge Barwick?"

"She's probably pretty far down the totem pole at the FDA, but she's the one who received Styralon's application for approval. Herrelson gave me her name and apparently gave her permission to do a filmed interview—*after* he checked up on my credentials at the station. I must have passed, because we see her in the morning and Herrelson the same afternoon. Maybe they'll have something to say about Daniel Bowen. Are you free?"

"I'll have to move some things around, but I think I can do it. You could have given me a little more notice, Miss Lenhart."

"Time, Mr. Weber. Time," Jessica said. "We can fly down and pick up a rented car at the airport. The crew will drive down. Ann is making all the arrangements. She'll call your secretary. And keep your cash in your pocket. This one's on me."

"Okay, Alice. On you."

NINE

As they drove along the highway that followed the Potomac north of Washington, she told Doug about her interview with Dr. Rudnick. "If he's half as good on camera as he was just talking to me, I can use him throughout the film. And he was a lot more skeptical about the system than Karl Engle."

"Did you mention Styralon?"

"I didn't have to. But I think he knew which drug I was talking about. You'll have a good witness in him. And there's something else I should tell you. I went to McCampbell."

"You did what?"

"I had to. And it was really very funny. I got their PR lady to sell Styralon to *me* as an idea for a film. Of course, she thinks it'll be a puff piece."

"God damn it! That's exactly what I was afraid you'd do."

"But that's how I found Karl Engle."

"And what happens when Engle checks back with his friends at McCampbell?"

"They had to learn about the film sooner or later. But they still don't know about your case."

"It was a stupid thing to do, Jessica. You can't run around manipulating people like that, just for a film. I wonder what you intend to do when I find a damaged child."

"Film him," she said. "I think we turn left here."

Madge Barwick was on a brief leave of absence from the agency, she had told Jessica over the phone, but she would be happy to be interviewed at her home if Jessica didn't mind coming out to McLean. The neatly drawn map she had sent in the mail lay unfolded on Jessica's lap. Spring had turned the trees a bright, light green along the highway. Suburban lawns were dotted with daffodils. Madge Barwick's house, like thousands of others that ringed Washington in the Virginia hills, was built of clapboard and brick in a style Jessica called Civil Service Colonial. The station wagon parked in the driveway announced that the crew had already arrived.

"Do please come in," Mrs. Barwick said, greeting them at her front door. "The gentlemen from your station have been telling me such amusing stories about their work."

Everything about Madge Barwick was as neat and precise as the map she had drawn for Jessica. Reddish-brown hair, precisely curled, framed her neat and pretty face. She wore a neat print dress, obviously chosen for this special occasion. And sprawled on the couch and chairs in her neat little living

"If such evidence had been submitted, would you have rejected the application?"

"I'm not empowered to reject anything if it's in the proper form. I would simply have passed the information on to the appropriate department."

Jessica made a wide circle with her fist, calling for a medium close-up. "Do you know Dr. Daniel Bowen?"

Again Mrs. Barwick seemed somewhat startled, but before she could answer, Jessica raised her hands, palms upward. The room was silent except for the hum of the camera and the whirring of the tape recorder. Whiteside shook his head. No, he wasn't picking up any extraneous sound. Then they all heard the drone of an airplane. Jessica signaled Spignole to stop the film as the plane roared directly overhead.

"I'm sorry, Mrs. Barwick. We can continue in a moment."

"Okay, Jess, it's gone," Whiteside said, replacing his earphones.

"Barwick, Take Two. You got speed."

"You were saying, Mrs. Barwick?"

"I've forgotten where we were."

"I asked if you knew Dr. Daniel Bowen."

"By reputation, of course," she said. "He's very famous in the field of drug testing. Many of his reports have been submitted to the agency and it's always such a pleasure to handle them. Everything in perfect order. That's why I was so surprised when I met him."

"You met Daniel Bowen?" Jessica asked, again circling her fist. "Recently?"

"Not too many months ago, Miss Lenhart. And it was very sad. I didn't expect him to be so old. And he seemed so nervous and troubled. I thought he was a very sick man. That's why I wasn't surprised when I heard he had retired from Chanterelle. He was in charge of the research on Styralon there, as I'm sure you know."

"Yes." Jessica's eyes connected briefly with Doug's before she said, "We have reason to believe that Dr. Bowen did not retire."

"I don't understand."

"We have reason to believe he was fired by Chanterelle."

"You mean just because he was ill?"

"We suspect Daniel Bowen uncovered information unfavorable to Styralon that someone did not want revealed."

"But Dr. Bowen's signature was on all the Chanterelle reports," Mrs. Barwick said, clasping and unclasping her hands in her lap. "At least to my recollection."

Jessica remained silent.

"Are you saying his signature was forged? That would be highly irregular. I'm sure you must be mistaken, Miss Lenhart. Research scientists are often very high-strung, suspicious of everything. If Dr. Bowen did have any concern about Styralon, perhaps he was proved wrong by the other researchers and that's why Chanterelle had to let him go."

"You've got one minute, Jess," Everett called out.

"Let's change rolls now. There are just a few more questions I'd like to ask."

Mrs. Barwick rearranged herself on the couch. "Am I doing all right? It's so hard not to blink with all this light."

"You're doing fine."

"Poor Dr. Bowen." Her soft voice trailed off into a whisper. "Such a nice man. And such a long and distinguished career. It's a pity."

"Okay, Jess, we're ready. Roll Two, Barwick, Take Three. Speed." Snap went the slate.

"To summarize your remarks, Mrs. Barwick, to your recollection everything concerned with Styralon's application for approval was completely in order."

"Oh yes. All the papers were in perfect order."

"Can you think of anything else you would like to mention?"

"Only that Styralon will help so many women, Miss Lenhart. A miscarriage is not something a woman gets over easily."

"And what is your opinion of the way the FDA operates?"

"Well, I've been there twenty years and it's a wonderful place. I know some people say we're too slow and too conservative. But the agency carries such an awesome responsibility. Sometimes I wake up in the middle of the night and think to myself, what if *I* made a mistake, what if *I* did something wrong? Think of the consequences. And I'm just an administrator. I wouldn't have a job with more authority than that for all the money in the world."

As the crew packed up the equipment, Madge Barwick signed the release form stipulating that she waived all rights to this interview and permitted the use of her likeness, words, and image on film and in all publicity for the film, now and in perpetuity.

Dr. Kenneth Herrelson kept them waiting outside his office for almost twenty minutes.

"You sure took a chance with Barwick," Doug said, still nursing his anger, "when you implied Bowen had been fired without a shred of evidence to prove it. A good defense attorney would jump on that as grounds for objection, possibly even dismissal."

Jessica was unconcerned. "Fortunately, we're not in court. I may not have any solid evidence, but my intuition tells me something's wrong. If Bowen did retire, or even if Chanterelle no longer needed him—for whatever reason—why would he vanish without a trace? Ann found his address in an old medical directory but he moved six months ago. And none of the medical societies he belongs to knows where he is."

"Dr. Herrelson can see you now," his crisply efficient secretary announced.

An American flag flanked one side of his desk, the seal of his agency hung on the wall, standard props in the offices of top-level Washington bureaucrats. But the youthful Dr. Herrelson, who wore a tweed jacket, and whose sandy hair was cut long enough to conceal his ears, did not seem to fit that image. "I've spoken to Mrs. Barwick on the phone," he said, barely taking time to acknowledge the introductions made by his secretary. "She said you believe there was some irregularity in our approval of Styralon. I assure you there was not. I see you're taking notes, Miss Lenhart. I'll have to ask you to submit them to me for my approval if you intend to quote my remarks in any way."

"Of course, I'll be happy to do that, Dr. Herrelson. Would you care to look at my list of questions before we begin?"

"That's quite unnecessary," he said, waving the paper Jessica offered him aside. "There's only one question I'll answer. You want to know if our agency has any evidence that Styralon is a teratogen. The answer is no, absolutely none. I took the time and trouble to have our files reviewed after you called, Miss Lenhart. I can assure you that any further inquiry along these lines would be futile."

Jessica put her pad and pencil aside, preparing for combat. "My question is not *if* you had evidence against the drug. I'm sure you didn't or Styralon would not have been approved. My question is *why* you didn't have it, when such evidence exists. I'm referring to recent studies in England where . . . "

"I am familiar with the English studies, Miss Lenhart," Dr. Herrelson interrupted. "Does that surprise you? Do you imagine that we live in a complete vacuum? But if you have read them as carefully as we have, you would know they are inconclusive."

"Yes, and I also know the agency requires that every new drug be tested for its teratogenic potential. Can I assume you were satisfied with the results of those tests for Styralon?"

"You can assume more than that. Our procedures and standards in that area are more stringent than anywhere in the world."

"Do you know Dr. Daniel Bowen?"

"Not personally," Dr. Herrelson said. "Only by reputation."

"And what is Dr. Bowen's reputation?"

"He is a very distinguished research scientist. He tested Styralon, as you know, Miss Lenhart. And that alone should reassure you the drug is not teratogenic. Now if you will excuse me . . . "

"Just a few more questions, Dr. Herrelson, if you don't mind. Has the agency ever approved a soft teratogen?"

He raised his eyebrows slightly, the first sign of any expression on his face other than impatience. "The answer to that question is obviously yes. There are many drugs on the market that if taken in massive, unregulated doses may have teratogenic potential. The agency cannot be responsible for the way a drug is used. Or abused, I might add."

"But the agency does weigh the risk versus benefit ratio in approving soft teratogens."

"I see you've done your homework, Miss Lenhart. Yes, the risk versus benefit ratio is a major factor in every area we consider. No drug, no matter what the law says, is ever one hundred percent safe and effective. You may quote me on that. Now if you will . . . "

"Just one more question, please, Dr. Herrelson. Has the agency ever been put under any pressure to approve a new drug?"

"Every day, Miss Lenhart, every day. Pressure comes from all sides. From the drug companies and their lobbyists, from special interest groups, individuals. A congressman whose wife has a terminal disease and who is convinced the cure lies in some unapproved medication from abroad. There is also pressure to rescind approval for a drug thought to be dangerous. But the FDA must remain impartial. It is like a court of law. And our mandate is specific. We are not required to prove that a drug is dangerous. It is up to the drug company to prove the drug is *not* dangerous."

Doug could no longer remain silent. "That's a twist on my understanding of our system of jurisprudence, Dr. Herrelson. In a court of law, a defendant is presumed innocent until the prosecution proves him guilty. The government appears to consider a drug company innocent until it gets around to proving *itself* guilty."

Dr. Herrelson's face was impassive. "That's an interesting interpretation."

"What if evidence from England *does* prove that Styralon is a teratogen?" Doug asked. "Would the agency act to ban the drug?"

"We would undoubtedly review our decision and call for further studies to be done here."

"How long would that take?"

"It's difficult to say."

"And if those studies proved unfavorable?"

"The drug would be banned."

"And how long would that take?"

"Again it's difficult to say."

"Would the agency consider initiating criminal proceedings, which I understand it's entitled to do by statute, if it can be proved that either McCampbell or Chanterelle did not provide full disclosure of their testing results?"

"Of course. Such information would be seriously considered by the agency."

"I don't mean to sound aggressive, Dr. Herrelson, or even hostile. But what if we provided your agency with proof of fraud, proof that they did *not* make full disclosure? Then would you bring action against the company, quite apart from banning the drug?"

"You don't sound aggressive, Mr. Weber. You sound like a lawyer. And if you are, I'm sure you know that no responsible party would bring such an action based on wild speculation."

"What if it's *not* speculation? What if I present you with someone damaged by the drug? What would the agency say then?"

"I do not think that would be a matter for this agency. If such a person could be produced, his appropriate recourse would be to make a claim against the drug company. And now you must excuse me. I have some important matters to attend to."

Doug's face was white with rage as he and Jessica left Dr. Herrelson's office. "That pompous, supercilious son of a bitch! Did you hear him? I want to hear him say that in court, in front of a crippled child, in front of his family."

Dr. Herrelson's secretary looked up from her desk and for a moment considered buzzing security. But she did not. She had seen many people leave Dr. Herrelson's office in much angrier moods than that.

Sara's car wasn't in the garage when he drove in. There was a note on the kitchen table. Ben poured himself a stiff drink and wandered through the empty house. The glass left a watery ring on the dresser in the bedroom where he changed into his worn yellow robe. In the kitchen, he scrambled some eggs, made toast—breakfast washed down with Scotch. Then in the living room, he wrestled with the uneasy sensations that came from being in the house alone. He felt like a stranger, an intruder who had no right to be there. Perched on the edge of the sofa, he hesitated before crushing out a cigarette in an ashtray. "Damn it," he muttered. "I live here."

Trying to make himself comfortable, he punched the sofa pillows and readjusted the lamp before he spread the contents of his attaché case over the coffee table. His eye caught a memo from Jessica that he found on his desk that morning. He had scooped it up unintentionally with the other papers he stuffed into his case.

To: Ben
From: Jessica
I'm at last on my way on this film and it's going well. I'll do two interviews in Washington today and fly home tonight. Ben, it's so thick, two films really. The monstrous defects in the children and, I suspect, the defects in the system that allow such a drug to be sold. While I'm concentrating on one aspect of the film, I feel I'm neglecting the other. But soon, they will converge, I know it.

The night of the fire, in the newsroom, I heard you ask for victims. That's what I need, too. But where? Probably in England, which I know will stretch our budget, but it will be worth it. And I must find a man called Daniel Bowen who tested the drug and who, I believe, has the answers I'm looking for. He has disappeared without a trace, perhaps a victim himself. Not of the drug, but something else. I'm not sure.

So that is the status of my work. You know the status of my love.

Her note, her initial at the bottom of the page, stirred feelings in him that were inappropriate to this house. She had obviously thought he would read it in the neutral zone of his office, for she had never encroached, never demanded intrusion here. Why had he brought it home? It made his mind taste and smell impossible things.

The sound of a car in the driveway startled him. Shoving the memo quickly into his attaché case, he felt he should shower, wash away the lust that had just come over him. He heard Sara's key in the lock, her soft footsteps in the front hall. She was still wearing her coat, the collar turned up around her neck, when she entered the living room.

"I'm sorry, darling," she said. "I didn't know I'd be so late. Have you had anything to eat?"

There was something different about her tonight, he thought. Her hair seemed lighter, her cheeks brushed with a color he had not seen in years. And the loneliness, the reproof he had seen in her early morning eyes was no longer there. She looked like a schoolgirl and suddenly he felt much older than she. "How was the lecture?"

"Interesting," she said. "All about me."

"You?"

"Yes. About women like me, frozen in time. Do you want a cup of tea?"

She took off her coat and left it on the chair in the front hall. A few moments later he heard the shriek of the tea kettle from the kitchen. It had been with them from the beginning, before the children were born. They had filled and emptied it in a hundred different cities, a thousand different rooms. And its piercing sound brought back memories of a time of mussed sheets, laughter in the afternoon, talks long into the night. Now they spoke in half sentences, unable to find words to express the old feelings or explore the new.

"Ben, the tea is ready," she called from the kitchen. "Do you want it out there?"

"No, I'm coming." He left his papers scattered on the coffee table. He would pick them up in the morning. And

Sara, he knew, would put the pillows back in their proper order. He thought of Jessica and the disorder of her apartment. But he was a very moral man and would not satisfy his hunger for one woman with the body of another. He and Sara would sit at the kitchen table, sipping tea, scarcely talking. And that would be that.

"Why are we here?" Jessica asked. "Is this where you live?"

"Once upon a time. Come on, get out. I want to show you something." Doug paid the cab driver who had brought them into the city from the airport, and they walked through the tall, wrought-iron gates guarding the campus of Columbia University. The darkness was punctuated with bursts of light coming from the buildings on the far side of the campus. Even at this hour of night, alone or in twos or threes, figures dotted the broad steps that led up to the domed library. "Remember the sixties?" he said. "This is where it all began. And ended."

"But why did you bring me here now?" Jessica insisted.

It was an impulse, a wish to explain his anger at Herrelson, to explain himself, a wish to be better known to her. "Something about Washington," he said. "All those damned buildings, and no one really knows what's going on inside. The buildings are impressive here, too, but for a couple of years at least, everything was out in the open. I was in law school and had worked damn hard to get there. My marginal economic status kept me from being a revolutionary. But I felt part of it. I saw it all happen."

"I was in Chicago in the summer of sixty-eight. I saw it happen there, too."

"Through the eyes of a camera?"

"In a way. I was working in television but I wasn't making films yet. It was very ugly."

"Not here," Doug said. "Not in the beginning. It was beautiful."

"Beautiful?"

"What a time it was. What an opportunity. A coalition between the smart kids with dough and the street kids who thought they had a chance, a visa for a better life, a college education. At first the street kids were too grateful to rail about the flaws of the system, grateful to have a shot at the highly touted American dream. It *was* a dream, and they thought it was only because the system worked that they were in college at all. But then something went wrong. The kids with the cars, with fat allowances from home, told them the system *wasn't* working. Leave home, leave school, leave the country—or tear it down. So they were confronted with an unnecessary choice: drop out or cave in. And either way they disappeared. Nobody bothered to say they could still be grateful for a shot at the dream and criticize the system. Nobody told them, including television."

"A camera sees," Jessica said. "It doesn't talk."

"That's my point. All the camera saw were the crazies who burned the flag or tore up their draft cards. The hippies, the drug freaks. And what happened? We lost a whole generation." He thrust his hands out at the dark and empty campus as proof. "Silent. Selfish. Do you remember Arnie Sultan?"

"Of course. He was in Chicago."

"I knew him here. He was the best who became the worst. He started out fighting for the right things in the right way. Then he became a celebrity and his only battle was to get his name in the paper, his face on the evening news. Television did that, too. He never had to go underground or spend time in jail. Arnie was too smart. And when he discovered he couldn't beat the enemy, he joined them. Just like I did."

"You?"

"Well, maybe ten years on Wall Street isn't joining the enemy. But that's where I was until I met Mel. And you know how he made me feel? Like I was a kid in law school, facing the same choices all over again. Only this time it wasn't an either/or proposition. He showed me I could do both: make the law work for others, not just for myself."

"That's how Mel makes me feel, too," she said. "Like a little girl dressed up in a woman's clothes, completely unprepared to take on the problems of the world."

"He says you never grow up until you become a parent. Have you ever been married?"

"No, it's eluded me. Why do you ask?"

"Just wondered," he said. "It's eluded me, too."

They had reached the other end of the campus and passed through the open gates to the street. "I remember police cars screaming through these gates," Doug said. "The crowds, the megaphones, the bedsheets hanging from the buildings. It's so quiet now. Maybe too quiet. Do kids care about anything these days?"

"Some do," Jessica said. "And some of them didn't care even then."

Speeding down Broadway, their cab lurched to avoid hitting a pothole and they were thrown together on the back seat. Caught by surprise, they laughed. But when the cab stopped for a light, they quickly drew apart and the space between them returned.

*R*iding up in the creaking elevator, Jessica took pleasure in the thought that she was coming to Kate's apartment as a friend, not as the confused young woman charged with the self-imposed task of filling her mother's loneliness. Kate's Sunday night dinner parties had become a regular event in her life, but she never knew what to expect or who would be there. The only certainty was that the food would be overwhelmingly ethnic.

Kate greeted her at the door clad in a billowing multicolored caftan. "Jessica," she exclaimed. "Early, of course. Not even Paul is here yet. But he's on his way from the airport. Come, let's chat a minute before the mob arrives."

She led the way down the hallway to her office and passing the living room, Jessica saw a great white Japanese lantern, her first clue to the evening's culinary motif. "How's Beryl?" Kate asked, taking Jessica's coat and tossing it on the narrow couch she used for her recumbent patients.

"Fine. Thriving plants. Even more jewelry. She's back to being herself."

"Any new electrical appliances?"

"Not since the toaster. Now it's cookbooks. The last one she sent was *Gourmet Menus for Two*."

"Mothers." Kate sighed with exaggerated dismay.

"You'd be out of work without them," Jessica said.

Kate laughed. "And your work?"

"I've started a new film."

"Love?"

Jessica paused for a moment. "One and the same. I know you think that's wrong. But for me it seems right. I'm the best I can be with Ben. We bring so much to each other: my involvement, his detachment, my sexuality, his lack of sexism, my idealism, his cynicism, my innocence, his experience. There are no artificial boundaries between us."

"But you can be only a part of his life. Are you willing to settle for that?"

"I'm not settling. I'm choosing. Twenty percent of Ben is better than all of anyone else. He's the earth and the moon to me, Kate, my love and my work, pulling together to create the tides of my life."

"On Thursdays." Kate's hands made a gesture of mock helplessness. "Why don't I just shut up? Maybe it's this room. Let's get out of here before I say something I'll have to charge you for."

Guests began to arrive soon after they returned to the living room, and in quick succession Jessica was introduced to a psychoanalyst with a thick accent and a thin wife, an elderly newspaper publisher who called the young woman on his arm "my old lady," a Belgian diplomat and his wife, and a single Japanese man who bowed from the waist and viewed the plate of raw fish that was being passed around the room with polite alarm. Then she began to lose track until, towering above the others in the room, she saw a bald head and heavy horn-rimmed glasses. Paul.

Tonight he was dressed in a pin-striped business suit, only one of his many disguises. She had seen him in corduroys and a turtleneck sweater, a dashiki and a Nehru jacket, among other costumes, all essential to his calling as the author of countless articles for journals of unorthodox opinion. He knew everyone, trotting from country to country, lunching with presidents and prime ministers, dining with cardinals and sheiks. And even when he destroyed them in print, he was always invited back.

"Jessica," he said, embracing her. "Beautiful—and alone, as usual. Who would you like to meet?" They always played the same game.

She surveyed the room quickly. "The man with the bow tie looks attractive."

"His sexual preferences are a matter of public record, my dear, and they wouldn't include you. I don't know why my wife doesn't make some effort to find you the right man."

"Maybe I've found him myself."

"Then where is he hiding?"

"He's not hiding."

"But he's not here."

"No, that would be impossible."

"Ah, finally the truth. Kate might have told me. If that's your style, I know a number of unhappy husbands who would be delighted to meet you. *And* take you to parties. Now, tell me about your work."

Kate, caftan flowing, swept down upon them. "I can't have the two most interesting people at the party talking to each other. Mingle."

They mingled and later met in the dining room where Kate was presiding over what could be described as a Japanese smorgasbord. No one dared tell her that her ethnic efforts, no matter how pure her intentions, were always a little off, one essential ingredient missing, or one added rhapsodically in a moment of creative ardor that was glaringly inappropriate. Her paella tasted vaguely Polynesian and the couscous served during her Moroccan evening the month before bore a strong resemblance to Bavarian pudding. Tonight, the tempura could have been mistaken for a down-home Southern fish fry. "One thing you can always be sure of when you eat my wife's cooking," Paul said to Jessica. "It's the first—and last—time you'll ever taste anything like it." To their surprise, the Japanese man seemed to be enjoying it enormously.

The party was almost over before they had an opportunity to talk again.

Paul was sitting cross-legged on the floor and when he remarked that his bones were permanently locked in that position, Jessica joined him. "I enjoy inviting important people to our parties," he said. "They always pretend they have someplace else to go and leave early. Now, tell me about your new film."

"I'm only at the beginning. But it's an incredible story. A drug has been approved by the FDA in spite of growing evidence that it causes birth defects."

"A teratogen," Paul said. He would, of course, know the word.

Jessica told him what she had discovered so far about Styralon while Paul rubbed his knees to stimulate his circulation and his bald head to stimulate his memory. "So you and your lawyer friend are playing a little game of pin the tail on the donkey," he said. "Bowen. Bowen. Why is that name so familiar?"

Staring into space, he searched through the archives of information stored in his brain. "Ah! I've got it. Last year in England one of the journals I write for asked permission to publish an article of mine earlier than planned because another article had to be withdrawn. It was about a drug whose name I don't remember, by a doctor whose name I do. Daniel Bowen."

"So he was silenced in England, too," Jessica said. "But by whom?"

"My poor innocent lamb. By other doctors whose reputations might suffer if the drug was discovered to be dangerous. By corporations that would stand to lose millions of dollars if it was taken off the market. But don't ask me for names. These people don't have names or faces. They sneak about like a pack of prowling wolves, one indistinguishable from the other. And they always attack the weakest member of the flock. Or the one foolish enough to think he can stand up to them alone."

"I don't think Bowen was alone, not in England. We know of other doctors there who are trying to stop the drug."

"Fine. Then it'll be easy enough to ask them where Daniel Bowen is. If I can't find you someone else's husband, my sweet, let me at least try to find the missing doctor. Don't bother to thank me. Just help me get out of this grotesque position or I may never walk again."

Kate joined them after saying goodbye to the last of the guests. "Don't ask me ever again to invite an investment banker," she complained. "I had to resist dragging him into my office and telling him just what his fixation on money really means. And what did you think of the fish?"

"Perfect," Jessica said. It was the only time she could lie to Kate.

"And who but you, darling," Paul said, "would have thought to add a pinch of cinnamon to the rice? A stroke of masterful invention."

"It tasted a little odd to me," Kate said. "But then, authenticity isn't everything."

Waiting for the elevator to reach their floor, Jessica kissed her friends. "Thank you, Kate. It was wonderful as always. And Paul, thank you for Dr. Bowen. Is there anything you don't know?"

"Oh yes, my dear, a great deal. I don't know, for example, why my esteemed colleagues in England killed Dr. Bowen's article. But I intend to find out. And I don't know why I'm hopelessly in love with a woman who expresses her deepest creative urges in the kitchen. Why not a coin collection, or even tropical fish? No, with my luck it has to be cooking."

ELEVEN

"Welcome to L.A.," the bellman said with a smirk that implied she was now in a far better place than whatever part of the world she came from. And picking up her portable electric typewriter he asked, "Out here to write a movie? Join the club."

Jessica watched him fumble with the keys to unlock her room. 1124. Was it coincidence, mere chance? When the door opened and she saw a vase of long-stemmed coral roses on the bureau, she knew it was not a coincidence at all. She and Ben had spent four days together in this room the year before and he took the symbols of their romance seriously.

Rooms, roses, champagne, favorite booths in favorite restaurants were rituals in the moments they spent together, intimate reminders when they were apart.

She unpacked, changed out of the clothes she had worn on the plane, and sat down at the white bamboo desk to write a letter. Two days after Kate's Oriental evening, Paul had called from Berlin. "Your Dr. Bowen is in Los Angeles," he said. "His friends in London gave me his address. They're very worried about him. As for my friends at the journal, they were told, when they made a routine check of his credentials, that he was old, ill, and completely unreliable. But the Styralon controversy is heating up over here. So once again, my dear, you've grabbed a tiger by the tail. And by the way, a famous cook, who shall remain nameless, is already planning an Indian excursion. So be prepared for an unusual curry."

It had happened before, Jessica remembered. After weeks of researching a film, the one piece of information she needed would come from a totally unexpected source: a friend who had a friend, even a chance acquaintance who had heard, read, or knew something she had not yet been able to find. She had written Dr. Bowen immediately and while waiting for his reply took the crew to Columbia-Presbyterian and spent a morning filming Dr. Lionel Rudnick in his laboratory. At his insistence, all mention of Styralon would be edited out of the interview. He had heard of the drug, he told Jessica, but had no firsthand knowledge of it. He could only speak of the known teratogens and their terrible effects. Even so, Dr. Rudnick's cheerful face and careful choice of words gave her the framework around which she could build the rest of the film. But once again she refused his invitation to visit the damaged children in the pediatric wing. They were not the victims she was looking for.

She and Jeff spent hours in the editing room, screening the

footage and taking notes on how it might be cut. With Ann she began work on the factual material that would have to be covered in the voice-over narration. She called Helen Lassiter in Maplewood hoping to arrange another visit to McCampbell. "I'm sorry, Miss Lenhart," Mrs. Lassiter said coolly, "but we cannot give you permission to film the Styralon Story after all. Our people were so excited by the idea that we've decided to make the film ourselves. I'm sure you understand." Jessica understood. Karl Engle had sounded the alarm and there would be no more interviews with anyone even remotely connected with the company. Nevertheless, she sent the crew to Maplewood to shoot exteriors of the ducks, and the flowers around the building that were now in full bloom. There was no reply to her letter to Dr. Bowen.

Doug was impressed by all she had filmed so far, even more impressed that she had located Bowen. But when her second letter also went unanswered and Jessica announced her intention of going to Los Angeles, he was skeptical and then angry, warning her that she could alienate Daniel Bowen by her intrusion. "You're worried about your damned film," he said. "What about my case? If he disappears again, we might lose him forever."

"But what if I can get him to talk to me *and* testify for you? Isn't it worth a try?"

He couldn't stop her. And Ben's journalistic nose for getting a story was as strong as hers. The card with the roses in her room wished her good luck.

She had written Dr. Bowen again before she left New York, to tell him the name of her hotel and the date of her arrival, and she was disappointed that there was still no message from him. Disappointed but not surprised. His telephone number was unlisted. All she could do was write another letter.

"Dear Dr. Bowen, I hate imposing on you again, but I have just arrived . . . "

No, scratch that. Too negative.

"Dear Dr. Bowen, I am in Los Angeles, hoping you will consent to talk to me about . . . "

That was wrong, too. The telephone rang. It was after midnight in New York; a hard time for Ben to be calling. Dr. Bowen?

"Jessica, you *are* here! You wretched person. And I had to hear it from Kate. When can I see you?"

Marilyn Helman was a refugee, forced to leave New York when her husband Lennie, an independent producer, answered the call of Hollywood. "Before you say another word, tell me what it's like. Spring in New York. So wet, so unpredictable. God, I abhor sunshine. What's in Bendel's windows and can you come to dinner tomorrow night? You haven't seen our new house."

"I'd love it."

"Wonderful. But I should warn you about Lennie. He's become a convert, running around with a copy of *Zen Life*, growing bean sprouts in his office, mumbling mantras in between stock quotations. And now in addition to gardeners and masseuses, we have a guru and a macrobiotic cook. Promise you'll remind me of who I am before I start driving down freeways in the middle of the night searching for my soul."

"I don't think I have to worry about your soul."

"Well, everyone out here is searching for something. Mainly sex or survival. God, the scrutiny, the microscopic examination of feelings. Oh, Jessica, just hearing your voice makes me remember a wonderful life of empty calories and meaningless relationships. Tomorrow at seven then. Someone will pick you up at the hotel."

After she hung up, Jessica went to the window and looked

down on the deserted streets of Beverly Hills. She walked to another window, like the woman who gazes at her reflection in one mirror after another, hoping that the changing light, a different piece of glass, will somehow alter her image. But no matter in which direction she looked, the view was the same. Empty.

The aroma in the air was sour, a fetid locker room smell, distinctly male. Dressed in a bright green velour jogging suit, obviously new, Mel bent over to tie the laces of his running shoes, also new. "Will you look at this goddamn outfit," he grumbled. "When I made that promise to Wanda, I didn't know she'd buy me something like this."

"Don't blame Wanda," Doug said. "She told me it was your doctor." He was dressed in baggy sweat pants and a gray T-shirt with "Columbia" barely visible across the chest.

"My doctor's a fool. If what he says about me is true, I'd be dead." He heaved himself off the bench and slammed his locker shut. "Come on. Let's get this over with."

Mel was exhausted, or pretended to be, even before they reached the top of the long flight of stairs that led to the oval running track. "I don't believe I'm doing this," he said. "Look at them." He gestured toward the men of all ages and shapes who were thumping around the track with open mouths and empty eyes. In the center of the huge room, other men twisted their bodies into unnatural positions, grimacing with exertion and pain. "Why are they doing this?" Mel asked. "To lose a pound, increase a biceps, prolong an erection? At least it takes a little skill to play handball."

"Shut up for once and just run," Doug said. He led the way onto the track and they began to jog, Doug carefully adjusting his speed to Mel's lumbering pace. After three laps, Mel collapsed against the wall. "Tired?" Doug asked.

"Bored," Mel answered, gasping for breath.

"Just a few more laps."

"Okay, but don't wait for me. It's embarrassing."

They started out again and Doug quickly left Mel behind, completed a full lap and caught up with him again. "Goddamn show-off," Mel muttered. "I can't take any more of this. I'll wait for you downstairs."

Doug accelerated his pace, trying to time his breathing to each jarring stride. His legs ached and his heart began to pound, but he couldn't get Mel out of his mind. He saw his scarlet face and determined smile. And then he saw another face the color of ashes. His father, the stranger, was dying.

It was over a year ago when his mother had called to tell him, and he wanted to feel more than the obligatory dull intellectual ache. He wanted to feel diminished. At the hospital, he found his mother sitting in a waiting room, smoking a cigarette, with the same uncomprehending look in her eyes that had always been there. "I'm sorry," he said.

"So am I. He wants to see you."

He was shocked by the withered figure of a man outlined beneath a sheet. Intravenous solutions dripping slowly through plastic tubes were keeping him alive. A blue plastic mask connected to another tube supplied his oxygen. His eyes were open and his fingers pulled the mask away from his mouth. "You're here. You came."

"Don't try to talk," Doug said.

"No, we were never very good at that. Do you still read books?"

"Yes."

His father nodded, breathing with difficulty. "We didn't expect you," he said.

Doug was not sure what his father meant, whether he was unexpected today or the day he had been born.

"We didn't expect you to be you," his father said, closing his eyes.

A nurse entered the room, replaced the mask over his face, and checked the machines that monitored his heartbeat and blood pressure. Doug followed his mother back to the waiting room.

"You don't have to stay," she said.

"Do you need money?" Doug asked.

"You don't owe him anything. And I can take care of myself."

What did he owe them? Nothing but his life. Everything else he had done for himself. And his legacy from parents who had not cared for each other and did not know how to care for him? An unfamiliarity with love.

The rhythmic pounding of his feet on the track jolted his mind back to the present. He thought of Wanda. "Get him out of that office," she said. "Go to the gym. He's got to exercise."

"We used to play handball."

"No, that's too strenuous. Jog, sit-ups, I don't know. Whatever men do in a place like that. Just something to keep his heart working. It's funny, isn't it? The last thing I thought I'd have to worry about when I married that man was his heart."

Mel had known it was a conspiracy but joined it gladly, welcoming another opportunity to please Wanda and intrude in Doug's life. He was almost fully dressed when Doug returned to the locker room, face flushed and streaming with sweat. "You know," he said, "this place really depresses me. In the old days, when I was your age, we used to come here to work out, talk about baseball and girls, flick each other on the ass with wet towels. The old men were always down in the bar or billiard room, cooking up their little larcenies

of the soul. Now they're here. And what do they talk about with their big bellies and limp cocks? Deals. They must come here for some kind of atonement. The smell is the penance."

"You're here for survival," Doug said.

"Survival is highly overrated. Strictly for movie stars and politicians. Take a shower. You look so healthy it's disgusting. I'll meet you in the bar and we can talk about girls."

Doug found him there, listlessly stirring a glass of orange juice with a swizzle stick. "Another one of Wanda's demands. My other wives did everything in their power to kill me. For some reason Wanda wants to keep me alive. Maybe it's because I don't believe in insurance."

"Or maybe she loves you."

"Who can figure out women?" Mel said with a deep sigh. "But there's one thing you know for sure. The dumber they are, the more complicated the drink they order. There is a definite correlation between dormant brain cells and a frozen pink Russian daiquiri stinger. I call it Shane's Law. Wanda drinks Scotch and water. And speaking of women, what's with you and Jessica?"

"She's in Los Angeles. Against my wishes, I might add, looking for the doctor who conducted the Styralon tests. We think he may know something the drug company and the testing lab don't want the government to find out. If they deliberately falsified or suppressed his report, I've got grounds for criminal action."

"Now that's progress," Mel said. "What do you think of the way she operates?"

"She has a kind of all-or-nothing attitude, doesn't she?"

"Passion?"

"Pragmatism. You talk about crippled children, she talks about camera angles."

"It's part of her job."

"That's the trouble. She's all business. Doesn't she have any feelings?"

"Sure. And she'll surprise you with them when you least expect it. Wanda's the same way. She can be talking about wallpaper and all of a sudden she wants to make love. Women. No transitions. That's Shane's Law Number Two."

"Anyway, she's smart," Doug said. "She's got a good mind."

"That's a switch. When I was your age, I noticed the body first and then the mind. I still do."

"The body's not bad either."

"Then you *have* noticed. That's progress, too. There may be hope for you yet. Drink up and let's get out of here. And do me a favor, will you? Tell Wanda I did twenty-five laps and wasn't even breathing hard."

"You're asking me to perjure myself?"

"No. Just tell a little white lie."

A Mexican chauffeur picked her up at the hotel and drove her in a white Mercedes at breakneck speed along the wide boulevards and up the narrow crooked roads that led to the hills above Los Angeles. There were three other white Mercedes parked in the driveway of the Helmans' house.

Constructed of stone and glass, the house was landscaped with the kind of exotic plants that grow in pots in New York. Inside, water trickled over a pile of rocks and flowed into the large illuminated pool on the patio. "We're renting it from a rock star who came on hard times," Marilyn Helman explained. "Remember our apartment on West End Avenue with all the lovely peeling paint and those adorable cockroaches? Can you believe that people actually live like this?"

Marilyn was dressed in black silk accenting the paleness of her skin in defiance of all the other women in the room who wore costumes of gauzy white cotton and had complexions the color of café au lait. It was a look of double messages. "I hate to turn you loose in this crowd. Lunatics, one and all, torn between narcissism and self-loathing. No, wait, you'll like the Albrittons. She's a poet, he's a plastic surgeon. And at least they read. They have the *Times* delivered every day, not just Sunday. That's the true test out here. Jonathan, Greta, this is Jessica Lenhart. She's from *New York*!"

"We were just talking about our new security system," the plastic surgeon said. "Photoelectric eyes around all the doors and windows, wires under the rugs. They even did something to the lawn. Now a canary can't walk on it without alarms going off."

"I feel much safer than I did with the dogs," the poet added. "You have to turn it on and off, but at least you don't have to feed it."

She overheard snatches of other conversations. "I wasn't sure I wanted to try it at first," a woman was saying. "But my therapist was right there at the same party and I had the most wonderful reaction after just one little sniff. Of course it makes your nose feel funny, but my doctor says it helps drain the sinuses."

"Three million gross the first week and then the bottom fell out," a man said. "Luckily we can unload it on television."

"Jessica. God, you look awful. New York does take a toll." Lennie Helman drew her aside and examined her critically. "Look at your eyes. You need more niacin. You need more E. How long are you here? I'll send you to my man in the Valley. No red meat and all natural foods. That'll clean the toxins out of your system. Look at me. I've never felt better in my life."

Lennie Helman had dyed his gray hair an unnatural brown and was at least ten pounds under his normal weight. "Now here's someone I want you to meet. Andrew Pollard, this is Jessica Lenhart. Andy's a screenwriter. Maybe you two can make a movie together."

"What kind of films do you make?" Andrew Pollard asked.

"Documentaries. What kind of films do you write?"

"I'm doing an original screenplay for Lennie."

Compared to the other men in the room, Andrew Pollard seemed friendly and familiar, self-contained rather than self-absorbed. He drank vodka, not the fruit juices that stocked Lennie's bar. And at the buffet he took roast beef and potato salad, not the raw vegetables and whole-grain mush. They ate at a small table outside by the pool where the twinkling lights of Los Angeles in the distance looked like glowing embers in the waste and ashes of a volcanic crater.

"What's your screenplay about?" Jessica asked.

"Love," he replied.

When it was time to leave, he offered to drive her back to her hotel. "I live in West Hollywood," he said. "It's right on the way."

"You've latched onto the only sane man on the West Coast," Marilyn whispered in her ear as they said good night. "Lennie and I are coming to New York soon, darling. Oh, how I miss it. I'll call you."

"Great. We can take a long walk through Central Park and get mugged."

Andrew's car was small and Japanese. "I'd like to show you my house," he said. "It's the way people really live out here. I can offer you a nightcap."

Jessica accepted his invitation. She was not indifferent to

overtures of male friendship. Andrew Pollard might have passed unnoticed through her life in New York. But here he was an original.

He stopped the car in the driveway of a small Spanish stucco house in a neighborhood of houses exactly like it. "In the forties and fifties a lot of famous writers from New York lived around here. I like to think I'm keeping up a tradition."

"Are you from New York?" she asked.

"Phoenix."

He apologized for the condition of the living room. "My wife took a lot of things with her when she left. These are pictures of my kids. Joshua, Jennifer, and Jason. They're back in Phoenix with my wife. Now what can I get you to drink?"

Jessica studied the photographs of his children while he was in the kitchen. They were blond, blue-eyed and smiling like their mother whose name, she read under one of the photographs, was Jean. Then she examined the room. There were faint outlines on the walls where pictures had been removed. Wires dangled from stereo speakers on the book-shelves, attached to nothing. The television set with a tiny gray screen fixed in the center of a huge oak cabinet was a vintage model. Jessica began to feel as if she were on an archeological dig, sifting through the relics of a previous civilization. Obviously, Jean had made off with everything of value.

"Joshua's in Little League," Andrew said, returning from the kitchen with their drinks. "Jennifer wants to be a veterinarian and Jason wants to be an astronaut. You'd like them. They're great kids. And I know they'd like you."

From somewhere between her shoulder blades, a wave of sadness moved through Jessica as she began to understand why he had invited her here. Without asking a single question about her, Andrew Pollard was filling out the long form of his life. She was merely a female presence, assigned to motherhood. Did he picture her at the airport, awaiting the arrival of his children for holidays and summer vacations, see her in this dismal little house, cooking their food and picking up their toys? Joshua, Jennifer, Jason—and Jessica. How did he know she wasn't a child killer—especially children whose names began with J?

"Where do you write?" she asked, hoping to steer his thoughts in another direction.

"The dining room," he said. "I'll show you."

The only furniture in the room was a card table and a folding chair. And the only picture on the wall was of the Crucifixion—the bleeding body of Christ in torment nailed to the cross.

"I'm Born Again," Andrew explained simply. "When Jean left me, I thought my life was over. I hated myself until Christ taught me how to love again."

Another J, Jessica thought. Jesus.

"I can teach you how to love," Andrew said, fumbling to put his arms around her. "Jean couldn't give me what a writer needs. I know you can."

She drew away from him, wondering how to handle this. Was he dangerous? Countless atrocities had been committed for the love of Christ. If this were New York, she could simply bolt and hail a cab to get home. Taxis did not cruise the streets of West Hollywood. "Andrew, I think I'd better go now."

He gave up easily in Christian resignation. "Of course. I'll drive you to the hotel."

It was only a few minutes away. Conversation was hardly necessary. But as Jessica moved to open the car door, he took her hand and tenderly pressed it to his lips.

The hotel clerk gave her a message slip along with her key. "Mrs. Daniel Bowen called." There was no number, no indication that she would call again. Damn. She had missed the one call she had been waiting for. *Mrs.* Bowen?

Why had she gone out? Why, even for a moment, had she been attracted to Andrew Pollard? For her mother? For Kate? A way of proving that the windows in her attic were open at least a tiny crack? Or for herself, the gesture of a woman in love with a man who is mortgaged? Even if there was no threat that the bank would call the loan, did she sense intuitively that she should make some perfunctory effort to avoid foreclosure?

Perhaps I have only a small part of Ben, she thought, as she got ready for bed. But it surpasses the whole of anyone else I have ever met. To love is not to possess. It is to surrender and share parts of ourselves. And who is to say that one part is more or less important than any other?

In bed, she thought again of Ben and the sweet smell of his roses washed over her, as if he was lying there beside her, his hands traveling her body, making her emerge once more out of a dark bath. She was fulfilled by symbols, released by memories. Tonight, that was enough.

TWELVE

There was something larger than life, unreal, about the vegetation of California. At the Farmers' Market, it looked grotesque. Strawberries the size of hand grenades, tomatoes as fat as bowling balls, asparagus as big as air rifles. Jessica wondered what chemicals had been pumped into the soil and water that nourished such monsters. Teratogens. The word had become permanently fixed in her vocabulary and her vision.

She discovered the small café where Bertha Bowen had suggested they meet and chose a table where she would be clearly visible, wondering what Mrs. Bowen would be like.

On the phone the day before, her voice had evoked an image of fragility and fear.

"Miss Lenhart?"

Jessica had not seen her approach, and would not have thought it was Bertha Bowen if she had. She was dressed in a simple yellow linen suit. Her bearing was regal, almost imperious, her hair white, her flawless skin unlined but marked by dark circles under her eyes. She was a woman of strength, Jessica decided. Still, there was fear in her eyes.

They ordered herb tea. Jessica, again bartering with food, suggested a salad, some pastry. But Mrs. Bowen declined and for a few moments studied Jessica in silence. Without knowing why she had called, Jessica could say nothing. She could only listen.

"My husband doesn't know I'm meeting you," Mrs. Bowen began. "And if he did, he would be furious. Still, there are moments when I think anger would be preferable to the way he is now."

Lifting the cup of tea to her lips, her hand trembled slightly. And catching herself in that graceless act, she stiffened her shoulders and said, "We've read your letters. And I think both Daniel and I sensed something about you, Miss Lenhart. How hard they were for you to write."

"I don't want to intrude," Jessica said. "But I believe Styralon is a dangerous drug and your husband can help me prove it."

"Yes, so you wrote in your letters and Daniel agrees with you. Styralon is a dangerous drug. But he's already done everything in his power to stop it. He can do no more."

"Is that why he was fired?"

"My husband was not fired," Mrs. Bowen said. "He was retired. Perhaps for good reason."

"But if he opposed the drug, why are all his reports favorable to Styralon? Are his signatures forgeries?"

to buy a basket of grapes as blue and lustrous as sapphires. Jessica's eyes followed her until all she could see was a flash of yellow in the crowded aisles of the market.

Ben leaned over the sink and splashed water on his face. It had been a hell of a day. His top anchorman had been seen having lunch with the news director of a commercial network, one of the camera crews got mixed up with a band of hostile demonstrators at City Hall, and the film Howard Tarr had billed as an uncompromising look at union corruption turned out to be a combination of prejudice and complaint, an indictment of the entire labor movement. Worse, the night that stretched before him would be joyless and empty. Sara was visiting her family in Ohio and Jessica, damn it, was still in Los Angeles.

The door behind him opened and closed. He looked up and saw Lyman Ellis's face reflected in the mirror, his Caribbean tan bleached yellow under the fluorescent lights. He had just returned from a think tank seminar of media executives on St. Croix.

"Ben, I thought I might find you here. Do you have a minute?"

"Sure, let's go back to my office."

"No, this is fine. What I have to say won't take very long."

Were they supposed to unzip, Ben wondered, for a friendly chat over adjacent white porcelain urinals? Or would they sit in adjoining stalls while he murmured, "Forgive me, Father, for I have sinned." It was clear from the expression on Lyman's face that something was wrong. And from their location. A men's room was not his usual style. Lyman pissed in private.

"Ben, do you remember about a week ago I mentioned that TML is considering a grant to the station?"

"Sure, among a lot of other corporations."

"This is the first time TML has ever considered such a grant. And it would be a large one. I've spoken to Brad Danziger a number of times to iron out the details. He's their president. In fact, we've become good friends."

"Congratulations, Lyman."

"They're not in order yet. That's why I wanted to speak to you."

"Fire away," Ben said, patting his hands dry with a paper towel.

"TML owns McCampbell Pharmaceuticals."

Ben merely shrugged. "So?"

Lyman had expected a different response. "Jessica Lenhart is investigating McCampbell Pharmaceuticals," he said impatiently.

The connection clicked in Ben's mind. He had forgotten that Jessica's drug was manufactured by McCampbell. Still he did not show any visible reaction. "So?"

"Perhaps you don't understand, Ben. Jessica interviewed a woman at McCampbell under false pretenses. She's insulted a scientist employed by McCampbell. And she and some lawyer have been to Washington threatening to bring suit against McCampbell and the government."

"That sounds like Jessica," Ben said. "And your friend Danziger is worried?"

"He's merely concerned. And so am I."

"Concerned about what? That if Jessica makes this film, Danziger won't sign the check."

Lyman's face colored with indignation. "That's not my concern at all. I'm merely trying to save Danziger and this station any unnecessary embarrassment."

"And how do you propose to do that?" Ben asked, his hands grasping the rim of the sink to control his temper. "Are you asking me to kill a film about a dangerous drug because the company that manufactures it is giving us a chunk of money? There are a couple of names for something like that, Lyman. Bribery. Blackmail. Not to mention censorship. I won't do it. I'll walk out of here first!"

Ben's angry words resonated from the tile walls of the men's room. Lyman did not flinch. "You're mistaken, Ben. And as usual you're letting your emotions get the better of your good judgment. I'm well aware of the issues involved here. And I'm not asking you to kill the film. I'm merely asking you to keep me informed."

"Informed?" Ben said suspiciously.

"When Danziger told me one of my filmmakers was investigating his company, I was taken completely by surprise. I don't like surprises, Ben. All I could say was that it was a coincidence. And that if the film came from your unit, it would be fair."

"Fair to a company that's knowingly selling a dangerous drug?"

"That, as I understand it, is merely Jessica's assumption. But if she can prove it, don't you think TML would be the first to act? Danziger has assured me that his company will give Jessica its full cooperation. In fact, someone from TML will be in touch with her when she returns from Los Angeles. They have nothing to hide."

"That's very generous of them."

"They can afford to be generous," Lyman said curtly. "And so can I. I'll ignore your accusations as well as your threat to resign. None of that was necessary. I just want you to keep an eye on Jessica. And I want to see what she's filmed so far."

"That's your right, Lyman. But you don't have the right to pass it along to TML."

"I'm afraid you must leave that decision to me. The station cannot expect to have their trust or financial support unless I'm completely open and aboveboard with Danziger.

That's all I've got to say, Ben. I know I can count on you, just as I'm certain you'll know how to handle Jessica."

Lyman vanished from the men's room as suddenly as he had appeared, leaving Ben standing at the sink with the feeling that he had been taken, lured into a no-man's-land and robbed of his papers and standing. What Lyman demanded was somewhere in the outskirts of journalistic ethics. And it smelled to high heaven. A toilet was the perfect place for that kind of talk.

Ben shook his head at his own reflection in the mirror and entertained an impulse to enter one of the stalls, flick a handle, and flush Lyman Ellis right down the drain.

She was going home. The disorder in the room reflected the jumble of impressions cluttering her mind, like pictures stacked against the wall of a gallery waiting for someone to hang them in their proper places. Her old friends, Marilyn and Lennie, and their guests paradoxically preoccupied by nutrition and narcotics, the sad smile of Andrew Pollard crucifying himself with loneliness, the haunting circles around Bertha Bowen's eyes and the tenderness that transformed her most prosaic gestures into acts of love.

If Dr. Bowen had lost both his work and his son, Bertha Bowen had lost a son and a husband. And she was fighting quietly but desperately to bring him back to life. Whether that battle was won or lost, selfishly Jessica could only think of her own battle. She was returning to New York without Dr. Bowen. She had not driven him away as Doug feared, but he remained out of reach, and the reasons why Styralon had been approved were as baffling as ever. Even more confusing, the new information she had obtained from Mrs. Bowen contradicted all her assumptions. Dr. Bowen had not been fired; it *was* his signature on the Styralon reports. None of it made sense unless Dr. Bowen was part of the conspiracy and his refusal to talk now was an effort to protect himself. Perhaps Mrs. Bowen was lying when she said her husband had done everything possible to stop the drug. What had he done? She knew only of the article for the English journal, but had no idea of what was in that article or why it had been killed.

No, Bertha Bowen was telling the truth. Of that Jessica was certain. But there was more to the truth than she had supposed. Doug was right: she was too quick to jump to conclusions. She could not alter reality, cutting and editing it as if it were a film. The eye of her camera captured only the surface of things. Bertha Bowen's eyes had told her that.

She closed the top of her electric typewriter and left it beside the door with her suitcase. Her bill would be waiting for her at the desk and she could imagine Ben's reaction when he saw it. "Jesus, Jess," he would say. "How can I justify this when you didn't bring back a single frame of film?" That would be his public comment. Tough and blustery. In private he would take her in his arms, laugh, and say, "Hell, I bet Lyman and Stacey bill the station for more than that just for the flowers at one of their dinner parties."

And Doug. What would he say when she told him she had returned empty-handed? Without Dr. Bowen, she had no film, he had no case. Doug didn't have to watch his words. There was no private side to their relationship. And he had been waiting for her to fail.

She tucked the room key in her purse and carefully closed the door behind her. Room 1124. She had been just as sad a year ago when she and Ben left this same room to return to a city of crowded streets and cruising cab drivers. A city where days of the week held mystical meaning. A city pressed for time.

The desk clerk handed her a telephone message along with her bill. Perhaps Daniel Bowen had changed his mind. No. Andrew Pollard wanted to know if she could join him and a few friends this evening at a Born Again disco in Burbank.

THIRTEEN

"And how's Max?"

"Thriving," Ann said. "I told you he was just resting."

"You've done something to your hair."

"I'm letting it grow. There comes a time when every woman has to stop looking at the world through bangs."

"What else is new?" Jessica had come to the office straight from the airport, stopping at her apartment only long enough to drop off her bags and typewriter, and change into New York clothes.

"Tarr's film about labor unions is a disaster. Ben's furious. He's been locked in the editing room with Jeff for two days trying to fix it. But he wants to talk to you. If not this afternoon, he said he'd call you at home tonight."

"Has Doug called?"

"You must be kidding. He never stops. He wants to see you, too." Ann searched for the pink message slip on her desk. "The Rosenthal Gallery around six, if you're free. You're a very popular lady."

"Not for long. Wait until I tell them Dr. Bowen wouldn't even see me."

"I'm sorry, Jess," Ann said. "Where does that leave us?"

"Nowhere. A dead end. There's still a chance Bowen will change his mind, but maybe you and I had better start looking for another idea."

"Or maybe there's another angle. See that pile of stuff on your desk? It's material on Styralon I had copied at the Academy of Medicine Library. And it seems somebody is very interested in my reading habits. The librarian got a call from a man who said he was working with us and asked for a list of the articles I was having duplicated. I had the strangest feeling when she told me. It's a little like somebody reading your mail."

"McCampbell," Jessica said. "They're the only people who know what we're doing and where we'd have to look for information."

"Possibly. But it could be someone else."

Jessica shrugged. "Who? Not Doug. We give him copies of everything."

"TML," Ann said. "Does that ring a bell?"

"I've heard of it."

"Didn't you read McCampbell's annual report? And I mentioned it in one of my memos. TML owns McCampbell."

Jessica remembered the memo, but not TML. And with McCampbell, Chanterelle, and her search for Dr. Bowen in the foreground, she had left the background hazy and slightly out of focus. "And you think TML has been checking up on you?"

"I know it," Ann said. "And they're interested in you, too. Mr. Arnold Sultan, Vice President and Chief of Public Information, wants to have lunch with you. Why's that name so familiar?"

"I don't believe it," Jessica said. "Arnie Sultan was a college radical in the sixties. A little before your time. But he was a master of the media even then. I knew he'd joined the establishment, but I didn't know which establishment."

"Will you see him?"

"I wouldn't miss it for the world."

"I thought so. That other folder has everything you ever wanted to know about TML. I wouldn't want you to stumble into that lion's den completely unarmed."

Perched on the window sill, Jessica began to read through the folder: clippings from *The Wall Street Journal* announcing recent acquisitions, an article in *Time* describing the global span of a corporation that manufactured and sold nothing but owned dozens of companies that did, an architectural critique of their new building on Park Avenue, a glowing biographical sketch in *Fortune* of Bradford Danziger, their "dynamic and aggressive" president. She heard Ann's voice on the phone.

"I'm calling for Jessica Lenhart. She would be delighted to have lunch with Mr. Sultan at his earliest convenience."

Jessica scanned the jagged Manhattan skyline visible from her window. Which of those blunt steel and glass cubes belonged to TML? And why hadn't Doug told her he was preparing to sue not only a relatively small drug company but also a corporate giant? Was he afraid she would start rapping on their doors, too?

"You have a date," Ann announced, "with Mr. Sultan

Monday at one o'clock in the executive dining room of the TML Building."

A light summer rain was beginning to fall, streaking the office window, blurring her view of the skyline. Now Arnie Sultan and TML were rapping on *her* door. Curiouser and curiouser.

The narrow gallery was packed with people, the sound of their voices magnified by the low ceilings and bare floors. Track lights illuminated an exhibition of photographs entitled "HUNGER," huge blowups in surrealistic color and grim black and white of victims of famine around the world: shriveled old men and women, children with bloated bellies and flies dancing around their eyes. The opening night crowd of "invited guests only" chattered among themselves, their backs to the photographs, while waiters circulated with trays spilling over with champagne and delicate hors d'oeuvres.

Doug studied a life-sized photograph of a small girl no more than three years old, locked in time on a rutted dirt road, her arms outstretched, twisting her body into the shape of a question mark. Mel was standing next to him. "Jesus," he muttered, "how can we let this happen?"

Wanda, snatching the glasses from the end of her nose, averted her eyes from the photograph. "It's obscene," she said. "And I don't mean the pictures. These people. Who are they? What are they doing here?"

"We hope," Mel said, "they'll be good for a few bucks." He was one of the sponsors of the exhibition.

"That's all they're good for," Wanda commented.

"I wouldn't be too critical," Mel said. "See that lady over there?" He pointed to a well-fed woman in a white fur wrap who was talking to Clive Rosenthal, the owner of the gallery. "She's bankrolling the exhibition, including the champagne. Her late husband made a fortune franchising fried chicken."

"You know the most fascinating people," Wanda said dryly. "Who else is here?"

"That tall woman with the cigarette holder and the little pansy in the white suit. They work for Jessica's station. They don't have any money, but they hang around people who do."

Maureen Hahn and Scott Mazden, whose head was swiveling like a radar saucer, spotted Mel. They left a knot of people at the center of the gallery and joined him in front of a photograph of a man prodding a skeletal cow with a stick. Introductions were made and Maureen drawled, "Aren't the pictures marvelous?" as if she were looking at a Cézanne still-life, a bowl of red apples.

"But where's our paragon of social protest?" Scott asked. "This place is a natural for Jessica. So much guilt, so much outrage."

Doug observed Jessica's colleagues with the detachment of a marine biologist studying a strange new form of sea life. For all her iciness, all her determination, Jessica was not like these two. "As a matter of fact," he said, "we're hoping she'll be here."

"Oh good," Maureen said. "Perhaps she'll bring a camera crew and make a film of all this."

They left, bearing down in tandem on Clive Rosenthal and the fat lady in the white fur. "That caps it," Wanda said. "I've had enough. Can't we get out of here?"

Then they saw Jessica enter the gallery, trying to close a balky umbrella. There seemed to be some disagreement with the man at the door because she didn't have an invitation.

Mel steered Wanda and Doug through the crowd to meet

her. "She's my guest," he said imperiously, while Doug took the umbrella from her hand and gently pressed the button that collapsed it.

"Welcome home, darling," Wanda said. "How was L.A.?"

"Like another planet," Jessica said. "I have bad news, Doug. I met Mrs. Bowen yesterday, but her husband wouldn't see me. We were wrong on a couple of counts. Bowen did retire and he did sign reports favorable to Styralon, even though he thinks the drug is dangerous. It doesn't add up, but that's all I could find out. A whole week wasted and now I'm stuck."

She spoke in a rush of words, barely acknowledging Mel and Wanda's presence. Then she said, "Oh, I'm sorry. This has to be boring for you. Doug and I can talk later."

"No, no," Mel said. "You two catch up. We'll have a glass of champagne and get depressed all over again looking at the pictures. Then we'll go to dinner. There's a great Italian place just down the street."

"You will *not* have another glass of champagne," Wanda said sternly. "And you will *not* stuff yourself with pasta. Doug and Jessica can fend for themselves. We're going home. Besides, who can eat after this?"

Mel rolled his eyes in mock dismay. "Ain't love grand?"

Wanda pecked Jessica on the cheek. "Good night, darling. We've opened the beach house. Can you come for a weekend?"

"When I finish this film," Jessica said, "which may be sooner than I expected."

"I'm sorry about Dr. Bowen," she told Doug after Mel and Wanda had left. "His wife tried to explain why he wouldn't see me. Their only child, a son, died not long ago and he's guilty and bitter about that. He's just given up the fight. But his wife is on our side and she may convince him to change his mind."

They sat on a low bench at one end of the gallery, shielded from the crowd by potted palms. "Did you know that McCampbell was owned by TML?" Jessica asked.

"Sure. Didn't you?"

"It didn't register until this afternoon. I got a call from them and I'm having lunch next week with their PR vice president. You'll never guess who he is."

"I give up. Who?"

"Arnie Sultan."

Doug burst into laughter. "I don't believe it. Arnie Sultan working for TML. So much for a brave new world."

"They've been checking up on Ann and probably on us, too, Doug. Doesn't that strike you as a little sinister?"

"I'd call it business as usual. The first step in any adversary proceeding is know thine enemy. The second, take her to lunch. Arnie Sultan will charm you right out of your chair."

"Maybe I can charm him into talking on camera," Jessica said.

"I doubt it. You won't find Arnie as fond of television as he used to be."

Jessica sighed. "Then that's it. All I've got on film are a couple of interviews that confirm the facts exactly as we know them. I feel so frustrated. How can we prove Styralon is dangerous? Is there anything new on your case?"

"Not much," he said. "You want to take a look at the pictures?"

They walked slowly around the gallery together, Jessica studying each photograph, Doug studying her reactions. There were none. Her expression remained coolly impassive, even before the little girl whose body was twisted into a perpetual question. Was she scrutinizing the lighting, he wondered, checking the camera angles? She took pictures; didn't she ever *see* what she photographed?

They were seated again on the low bench, Jessica oblivious to the noise of the crowd and the waiter who offered them champagne. Finally she said sadly, "Why is it always the children who suffer? Famine, war, disease. So many horrors. I thought Styralon was one horror we could stop." She stood up suddenly. "Forgive me. I'm tired. It was a long flight. Are you ready to go?"

"Jess, wait a minute." He took her hand and pulled her back down on the bench. "There is something new on the case. They've found two families in London, each with a child who was almost certainly damaged by Styralon. Both mothers took the drug in the first five weeks of pregnancy. I'm going to England next week, and if I can convince them to testify for me, I've got a case. Even though the children are British, they are Persons with Standing in our courts."

Jessica's mood changed instantly. "Doug, it's what we've been waiting for! Why didn't you tell me? Let me come with you. Then I'll have a film."

"I knew you were going to ask me that. The families may not agree to talk on camera, Jess. They may not agree to testify for me. They're already taking depositions over there. Then there will be the ordeal of the trial. That's a hell of a thing to put any family through."

"That's my point," Jessica interrupted. "Couldn't you use my film as evidence here if they don't want to testify in person?"

"I'm not sure how the court would feel about introducing a film as evidence. And how would you feel about letting it be used in an adversary proceeding? McCampbell might find some way to turn it against us."

"It may be months before you get into the courtroom," Jessica said. "McCampbell and TML have won every round so far, including Daniel Bowen. But a case in the English courts and a damaged child on film wouldn't be so easy to cover up. We might be able to kill the drug with that kind of publicity even before you go to court. Or at least jolt the FDA into action."

"And you'd make your air date."

"To *hell* with my air date!" Jessica said angrily. "Don't you realize that ten minutes ago I thought we didn't have a chance? Now we do. Even Bowen might come forward now. We can win, Doug. You've got to let me come."

He was surprised by her passion. "All expenses paid?" he asked.

"Please, Doug, don't make me beg all over again."

"Okay, okay," he said. "I'll find out if the families will talk to you. That much I can do."

Heavy rain was pounding the canopy over the sidewalk in front of the gallery. A row of limousines was parked at the curb, engines idling. The few cabs that passed were occupied or off duty. "How about dinner?" Doug said, trying to discover the trick that opened Jessica's umbrella. "I think I know the place Mel was talking about."

"Thanks," Jessica said, "But I've really got to get home. I can take the bus at the corner."

Walking toward the bus stop, they passed the lighted windows of a toy store. A stuffed giraffe nibbled a plastic leaf; monkeys with idiotic grins hung from the branches of cardboard trees; a lion crouched in the erzatz underbrush. Jessica frowned, tightening her grip on Doug's arm, while he held the umbrella high to protect them both from the pelting rain.

They huddled in the doorway of an office building until they saw a bus approaching. "Here's your umbrella," he said.

"No, you keep it," she said, darting for the bus.

He stood on the corner, his shoes wet, his pants drenched up to the knees, rain dripping from the ribs of the umbrella soaking his shoulders. Mel was right about women. No transitions. But until tonight he had thought there was only one Jessica. In the gallery, he caught a brief glimpse of someone else.

Perhaps in London they would be introduced.

The phone was ringing as she entered her apartment. Stepping over the bag she had left in the hall, she grabbed it and said a breathless "Hello."

"Jess?" It was Ben.

"I just walked in the door."

"I know. I've been calling."

"I'm sorry. I had to meet Doug Weber. Are you still at the office?"

"No. I'm at Ernesto's. Can you meet me?"

"Of course. Just give me time to change. I'm soaked."

Ernesto's was one of the small Village restaurants they frequented on Thursday nights. The headwaiter's greeting did not conceal his surprise at seeing them there so early in the week.

The bottle of wine on the table was open and half empty. Jessica tasted it on Ben's lips when he kissed her. "I thought you'd never come back," he said.

"How much time do you have? When is your train?"

"Forget the train." He poured her a glass of wine. Sancerre, another ritual. "I need you tonight, Jess."

"I've missed you, too. Thank you for the roses. But somehow Room 1124 wasn't the same without you."

"It's been one hell of a week. The unit is falling apart. Higby is thinking of bailing out, and Lyman probably won't let me replace him. And I damn near fired that son of a bitch Tarr."

"Ann told me."

"I don't know why I'm dumping all this on you. Let's order and you can tell me about California."

Sensing his gray mood, she tried to cheer him up with stories about the Helmans and her encounter with Andrew Pollard. It worked. "What do you do at a Born Again disco?" Ben said, choking with laughter. "Dance the Resurrection Hustle? Oh, Jess, it's so good to see you. You're an intoxicant. No, that's wrong. You're too necessary to be a mere intoxicant."

She waited until their dinner was served before telling him about her meeting with Bertha Bowen. But he seemed distracted during her story, his thoughts somewhere else, and a curious expression crossed his face when she said she had come back to New York certain she couldn't finish the film. "But, Ben, the most incredible thing has happened. You know Doug and I have been looking for a child damaged by the drug. Now he's found two of them in London. If the families agree to talk to me, I'll fly there next week with Doug, hire a free-lance crew, and make my air date with time to spare."

"London?" Ben didn't seem to share her enthusiasm. "What did California cost? And now a trip to London. I'll have to clear it with Lyman."

"Lyman? Why? Since when do we have to clear anything but our ideas for films?"

"Jess, the unit's already over budget."

"I've never seen you like this," she said. "We can't let the budget stand in the way. I *have* to go to England."

"I'll swing it. Don't worry."

The rain had stopped by the time they left the restaurant. Wet pavements sparkled under the street lamps. The air was fresh with the smells of early summer. They kissed as soon as they reached her apartment. Ben pressed her close against him, his attaché case bouncing lightly against her back. It was a sensation associated with their farewells. "When is your train?" she asked.

"I can stay, Jess."

Her head tilted up, her expression incredulous. A whole night? Breakfast together in the morning? He had surprised her with this jewel, this present of hours.

He began to shed pieces of himself, his jacket, his tie. He put his watch and wedding ring on the coffee table. At first he had left them on the small table by her bed until one night they caught the dim light, reminding them both of time and his other commitments. Since then he had left them in the living room.

He went into the bathroom to shower while Jessica closed the curtains and then peered into the refrigerator. What would she serve him for breakfast? There was nothing but coffee and a loaf of bread. The one-slice toaster would at last be called on to do double duty. Beryl would be pleased.

Returning to the bedroom, she was filled with the expectancy that never seemed to diminish, anticipating the magical combination of discovery and familiarity that was such an extraordinary part of their lovemaking. Hands somewhere, lips somewhere else, creating her, bringing her to life.

He was singing in the shower. "Please," she called out. "Think of the neighbors. I have my reputation to consider."

"I want the whole world to know," he called back. "I'll skywrite it: 'Ben and Jessica still going strong after four years.'"

In bed, he wrapped her in his arms with unexpected intensity. She drew away from him, stroking his fine hair, still damp from the shower. In the candlelit restaurant his face had looked tired, the lines around his eyes and mouth drawn deeper than she remembered. Now he was himself again.

"Jess," he said, as if he could read her thoughts, "you bring me back to life. No, back is not the word. Even years ago, it was never like this."

"Never?"

"Never."

He made love to her with abandon, recklessly. And she sensed that somehow he had changed. He had never been so explicitly ardent, so specifically passionate. Was it because they had the whole night ahead of them? Had he called Sara? She could not ask questions like that, for they would imply she did not understand him, that she was demanding more than he had already given her. She could only abandon herself to him and the intensity of his love.

They were curled up together under the light cotton comforter. "We should have bought the paper," he said.

"It's delivered in the morning."

"I always buy mine at the station."

That was something about him she had never known before. Another discovery, a ritual they did not share.

"Something very funny happened to me today," she said. "Well, not funny, really. I made a date with Arnie Sultan for lunch."

"Arnie Sultan? I haven't heard that name in years. What's he doing without a revolution?"

"He's some kind of front man for a corporation called TML."

She felt his body stiffen slightly. "What's the occasion?" he asked. "Is he celebrating his new respectability?"

"Ben, TML owns McCampbell. They've found out about the film and they're checking up on me."

He rolled over and stared at the ceiling. In the darkened room Jessica could not see the expression on his face. She sat up and turned on the light. "Ben, what's the matter?"

He touched her cheek, his hands lingering on her throat. "Nothing, Jess, nothing. Now turn off the light and come over here. Or do I have to remind you of the virtues of a second course?"

∽ *FOURTEEN* ∽

"*I*t used to be that a guy could walk through an airport and forget the cares of the world," Doug complained.

Checking in for their departure at Kennedy, they had been accosted by three crew-cut young men advocating nuclear power and the abolition of the Supreme Court. Then two saffron-clad Hare Krishnas with shaved heads and empty smiles thrust flowers and pamphlets at them. And finally, an old woman with blue hair begged them to sign a petition banning abortion.

Seated now in the comparative quiet of the first-class lounge, Doug asked, "When did it happen, these hordes of political and spiritual deviants hanging around airports?"

"There was probably somebody soliciting at Kitty Hawk," Jessica said.

"But these people are planted. Someone is paying them, printing the posters, buying the flowers. And you may have noticed they have nothing to do with the plight of the poor or the oppressed."

"Even anarchists need organizations," Jessica said. "Like your old friend Arnie Sultan."

On the cab ride to the airport, she had amused Doug with a description of her lunch with Sultan in the executive dining room of the TML Building, where security was tighter than at an embassy in a hostile foreign country. A private elevator whisked her to the forty-eighth floor. Expecting an expansive view of Manhattan, she found instead a cozy room designed to resemble a New England country inn, complete with fireplace, wood paneling, and exquisite antique furniture. The tables were set with linen, silver, crystal, and sprays of wildflowers. TML was deeply rooted in Americana.

"I hope I didn't keep you waiting," Arnold Sultan said when he joined her. "May I call you Jessica? And please call me Arnie."

She would never have recognized him. Shorn, clean-shaven, manicured, conservatively dressed. Jessica had a fleeting memory of his student radical days. The flying hair, the beard, the revolutionary rhetoric urging a generation into noisy rebellion. Small, suspicious eyes were the only vestiges of his former self.

After they had ordered drinks, he said, "I admire your work, Jessica. You've made some fine films. When we heard you were interested in Styralon, we knew you would examine both sides of the issue with fairness."

His strategy was immediately apparent: flattery linked to an appeal for simple justice. "Then you agree," Jessica said, "that there are some grounds for controversy about the drug."

"There are two sides to every question," Arnie replied. "It took me a while to learn that."

Now that he had reminded her of his revolutionary past to reassure her that he, too, had a social conscience, she knew his next step would be to pitch TML as a paragon of principle.

"I wanted to meet you," Arnie continued, "to guarantee our complete cooperation. Most corporations wouldn't be willing to do that. But we're an exception. As individuals, and as a company, we're acutely aware of our responsibilities."

The waiter returned, and addressing Mr. Sultan by name, recited the menu. "I can recommend the Yankee pot roast," Arnie said.

Over lunch, served with a bottle of vintage wine, he became more expansive. "Big business no longer has the power it used to have, Jessica. Today *we're* the underdog, controlled almost to the point of paralysis by government regulations, constantly scrutinized by the media and special interest groups. We forget how much this country owes to big business. Without it there would be no charitable foundations, no museums, no opera." He paused for emphasis. "No public television."

Jessica was enjoying the food—it was delicious—just as she was enjoying Sultan's performance. But she had not anticipated threats until much later in the conversation. "At my station," she said, "we're usually not concerned about where the money comes from. It's a way of insuring our integrity and independence."

"And that's just the way it should be," Arnie said jovially. "May I ask what you've been able to find out about Styralon?"

"Not much," Jessica replied, guessing that he already knew the answer to his own question. "In fact, I may not have a film at all, unless . . . Well, frankly, Arnie, your offer to help has come at just the right time."

"What can I do?" he asked eagerly.

"I'd like to interview the people at McCampbell who made the decision to manufacture and sell the drug."

"That can be arranged, but you must know that a lot of people are involved in making decisions like that. No single individual is responsible."

"I see," Jessica said. "I'd also like to review the records of McCampbell's business relationship with Chanterelle."

"I'm not sure such records exist, but I'll try to find out."

"And the results of both McCampbell's and Chanterelle's tests."

"That's easily done," Arnie said. "The FDA has those."

Jessica heard the soft click of doors being politely closed in her face. "Is there someone who would consent to talk to me about the actions your company would take if Styralon does prove to be dangerous?"

"*I'm* talking to you," Arnie said, and she heard another soft click. "And I can reassure you we would act swiftly. We're aware Styralon is controversial. Almost every new product is. We're no stranger to controversy, but we do wonder what your purpose is in making this film?"

Jessica pretended to consider her answer, suspecting that TML's sole interest in Styralon was whether it would improve McCampbell's profit picture or become a costly embarrassment. "I'm simply looking for the truth," she said finally.

"Aren't we all?" Arnie agreed. "And even though there's

no real proof the drug is dangerous, you intend to keep looking?"

"Yes," she said. "That's my job."

Arnie glanced at his thin gold watch. "I admire that. And I can certainly give you all the information you'll need. We're a remarkable company, you know. I'm proof of that. Not many organizations of this stature would have hired me."

"I'm surprised," Jessica said, carefully choosing the right tone, "that you would even consider working for them."

"It does seem strange to some people. But I see no conflict. I always said the way to change the system was not to destroy it, but to work from the inside. That's what I'm doing here, molding the company's image and urging them to take a larger part in public-spirited activities—like contributing to your station."

It was the second time he had mentioned the power of his corporate purse, and a second mention of the strength of his own social commitment. Apparently he saw no contradiction, Jessica thought. But he had made his point clearly enough. TML would be more comfortable if she dropped her investigation, and if she continued, they were prepared to make it uncomfortable.

"What's your next step?" Arnie asked. "Are you interviewing anyone else?"

"At the moment, I have no immediate plans. I'll have to wait until I hear from you."

"Fine. I've already started putting together some information for you. And I'll see what I can do at McCampbell. But it may take a little time."

"That's wonderful," Jessica said. "I'm very grateful."

There was no check. Arnie Sultan did not leave a tip. He merely nodded to the waiter as they left the dining room. The uniformed elevator operator waited while he took her hand and said, "It's been a great pleasure meeting you, Jes-

sica. We both do good things. You in your way, I in mine."
She returned the gentle pressure of his grip. "You're right,
Arnie. The only difference is for whom."

"That oily little bastard," Doug said. "He hasn't changed
a bit. If he tries to intimidate you in any way, I'll add it to
my brief."

"They must know what you've been doing, too," Jessica
said. "Maybe Arnie will take you to lunch. The pot roast
was good."

There was a delay in the plane's departure and liquor
flowed freely in the first-class lounge. "Why," Jessica asked,
"do airlines prefer their passengers in a state of total intoxi-
cation?"

"I don't know, but it's the only way I can tolerate the
food."

Their flight was finally announced and they went through
the rituals of boarding and takeoff. Then they were airborne
and the details of the sprawling city gave way to the flat
black of the ocean. Jessica turned her eyes away from the
window when there was nothing more to see. "I always feel
as if I'm in a cocoon on airplanes," she said. "Snug, but very,
very fragile."

Doug unfastened his seat belt and stretched. "It's a long
flight. Who knows what we may turn into?"

"What's your schedule tomorrow?"

"I'm meeting with the lawyers. They have depositions
from the doctors and the two families. The Barretts won't
see you or me, so the Harcents are all we've got. You might
want to read their deposition before you interview them."

"How old is their little boy?"

"About four."

"I'm meeting the crew. I want to talk to them before we
descend on the Harcents."

cent. And their son Timmy. Again she would barge into people's lives, directing them to exhibit their anguish for her cameras. She had found her victim; she could finish her film. Why then did she feel like an organ grinder commanding his monkey to dance with cruel flicks of the chain around its neck?

In the dim light of the room, Arnie Sultan's red roses looked black, as black as the thought behind them, as dark as her own mood. She had to conceal her self-doubt. And she promised herself that, tomorrow, no one, not the boy, not his parents, not the crew, and certainly not Doug, would see how she really felt. Or she would surely fail.

Through the rear window of their rented car, Jessica could see the van behind them, with the cameraman, Kevin Lochner, at the wheel. They were lost in the maze of a working-class district in the northern outskirts of London. When they finally found the street they were looking for, and then the house, it was like all the others in the neighborhood—gray-brown brick, window boxes overflowing with geraniums, the front yard planted with even more flowers. Doug parked at the curb and the van pulled in behind.

Jessica got out and spoke to Lochner. "Just give me ten minutes," she said.

"Don't worry, love," he said. "I guarantee pretty pictures."

Pretty pictures, she thought. Pretty pictures of a deformed child to take back to New York, to store in her own collection of captured injuries.

Laurel Harcent was waiting for them in the doorway even before she and Doug started down the flower-lined walk. She was a small, thin woman, her hair the soft red color of apricots. "Please come in," she said. "Timmy can't wait to meet you. He has something to show you."

She led them down a short hall, through the kitchen, and onto a porch overlooking the back garden. "They're here, Timmy," she called.

Jessica saw his father first, standing beside a small slide that had been set up in the yard. And then she saw the boy, perched at the top. He waved and pushed himself off. From a distance he looked like any other child until he stood up at the bottom of the slide on only one leg.

His father handed him his crutches and Timmy seemed a little impatient with his assistance. He tucked them under his arms, one of which looked as if it had been amputated above the elbow. The other, the one he had waved at the top of the slide, was withered. He made his way toward them nimbly, showing off, but he stopped at the porch and allowed his mother to help him up the steps.

"Will you take my picture on the slide?" he asked.

"I certainly will," Jessica said. Her voice sounded strange, even to herself.

"Now, no more nonsense, young man," his mother said. "There won't be any pictures at all until you get yourself cleaned up."

"Miss Lenhart," his father said. "I'm Bob Harcent. Can you and me have a word together? You, too, if you're the lawyer."

He looked older than his years. His color was sallow and his shoulders stooped. Jessica felt the tension in her body as she and Doug sat in the chairs he offered them around the kitchen table.

"I don't know how to say this," he began, "but Laurel and me have had a long time to think about it, and we're of one mind on this matter. We know why you want to take Timmy's picture and why you want us to testify in court. And we're willing to do it. It's not for the money, though God knows a little more of that would be a help. It's to stop things like this from happening. But he's our son, and we won't have you making some kind of freak out of him. He's got enough of that ahead of him as it is. And we won't have you making a little pet out of him, either. We don't want your sympathy and we don't want your pity. The boy's got to learn how to do things for himself, just like any other boy."

"I think we understand, Mr. Harcent," Doug said.

"That's fine then. I got that off my chest. But there's one other thing. My boy is pretty smart. He'll work his way around you, if he thinks he can get away with it. You have to watch that."

Doug sat with the family in the kitchen, talking about cowboys and Indians to Timmy, while Jessica and the crew set up their equipment in the living room. "Do you have a filter for the lens?" she asked Lochner. "If you don't, everything will look green in this light. And I don't want to pick up the noise of the traffic. Did you bring a shotgun mike?"

The crew looked at her curiously. Was she new at this business or did she think they were? "Are you going to mike the boy?" the soundman asked.

"No," Jessica said abruptly. "Have you checked the fuses?"

Lochner placed his large hands on her shoulders. "Relax, love. We've done this before, you know."

She drew away from him. "I'll check the light in the garden."

Passing quickly through the kitchen, she averted her eyes from the table where Doug was trying to explain American football to Timmy, whose high-pitched voice and delighted laughter filled the room. In the small back garden, she circled the miniature playground the Harcents had built for their son: the slide, swings, a sandbox, trying to think only of light, camera angles, and the questions she would have to ask, postponing the moment when she had to begin the interview.

How could she go through with this? She felt the same wave of disturbing feelings that had swept over her when Dr. Rudnick asked her to visit the children in his hospital. But now she realized it was more than that, a darker emotion she struggled to understand. Timmy was not a pathetic white mouse. He was a little boy. And she recognized, to her horror, that she wished he could be more pathetic, more damaged. He was not her ultimate victim.

She looked back at the house. It was too normal, too ordinary. Timmy was too cheerful, Laurel and Bob Harcent too gentle, too hopeful. She had wanted all of them to be more damaged. She wanted heroism, injury, suffering, rage. How could pictures of love and acceptance make her point? How could this appealing little boy win the sympathy of her audience, or Doug's jury?

Staring up at Timmy's slide, she again saw him at the top, waving. How could she, even for a second, have wished him to be anything but perfect, whole? Surely it's not me, she thought. It's my business. Television demands shattering pictures of violence and its victims, demands riots, fires, disaster, death, each picture more horrible than the last to stir even an instant of emotion. It's the people who watch television who can respond only to blatant suffering, exaggerated outrage. There's no room for Timmy as he is in my medium, or my country. Otherwise, the message will be lost.

Standing there, her forehead pressed against the edge of the slide, she was seized by an even grimmer truth. What kind of woman am I, what kind of woman have I become, that I am disappointed not to find this family drowning in despair? What have I done to feed the monstrous maw of television? How could I have thought I would have a better film if Timmy really were a monster? *I* am the monster.

"Jess?" Doug called. "We're all waiting for you."

"I'm sorry. I was checking the light."

Slowly she returned to the house, to find Timmy already sitting between his parents on the living room sofa. But he jumped down again to examine the camera and inspect the lights, then asked the soundman if he could wear his earphones.

"Timmy," Bob Harcent said sternly, "stop making a nuisance of yourself."

Laurel Harcent patted the sofa and he climbed back up, putting his head on his mother's lap. "Now sit up straight, like a big boy," she said.

"All right, love," Lochner said. "It's yours. Roll One, Take One, Rolling. Speed."

In response to Jessica's questions, Laurel Harcent told her story in much the same way it had been recorded in her deposition. Jessica was interested in more than the bare facts of the case. She wanted to know how the Harcents felt when they first saw their child. Did they blame themselves, did they pity him and each other? Did they believe he was merely an aberration, and they the losers in a game of genetic roulette? Did they wish he had been born dead? But she couldn't ask questions like that, not with Timmy sitting there.

"It was three months before we could bring Timmy home," Laurel Harcent said. "Then we almost lost him. It was his heart. They couldn't operate. He was such a tiny baby. That came later, when he was two. Do you remember when you were in the hospital, Timmy?"

The little boy nodded solemnly.

"The doctors saved him, thank God," Bob Harcent said. "We had our son."

They had answered her unspoken questions.

"When did you first learn that it might have been more

than an accident?" Jessica asked. "That a drug you had taken during your pregnancy might have been at fault?"

Bob Harcent thought for a moment. "About a year ago was when doctors and lawyers started talking to us. We didn't want anything to do with them at first. We just wanted people to leave us alone."

"Besides, they weren't sure it was the drug," Laurel Harcent added. "And I didn't believe it, either. I just couldn't imagine a doctor giving me medicine that would do something like that."

"What made you change your mind?"

"The doctor who gave me the drug came to see us," Laurel Harcent said. "He had all my records and wanted our permission to give them to these other people. He told us he didn't know how many women had taken that drug, but they were trying to locate all of them because they thought it was dangerous and ought to be stopped."

"I wanted to kill him," Bob Harcent said fiercely. "I wanted to crack open his skull with a hammer, that bloody bastard. How much did we have to pay him? How long did you have to wait for an appointment? It didn't matter then. We wanted the best."

"He didn't know, dear," Laurel Harcent said, trying to calm her husband's anger. "Nobody knew."

"They *ought* to know! What are we, guinea pigs?"

Jessica's voice felt thick. "What was your reaction, Mrs. Harcent? Were you angry, too?"

"I cried. I think I cried for three days until there just weren't any tears left. You remember that time when Mommy was so sad, don't you, Timmy?"

"I tried to cheer you up," Timmy said.

"And you did, darling. You always do. I blamed myself, you see. I wanted Timmy too much. I should have been more careful. I should have asked more questions. It was a terrible time, the worst time between Bob and me in all our years together. But we had Timmy. And we had each other. That's all that really mattered. These things happen. There was nothing we could do about it."

"But there is something you can do," Jessica said.

"Yes, the lawyers convinced us of that. I took no other drugs when I was expecting Timmy. There was no history of such things in Bob's family or mine. They said they needed us to prove the drug is dangerous."

Timmy was growing restless, fidgeting and squirming on the sofa. "When are you going to take my picture on the slide?"

Jessica looked over at Doug. "Do you have any questions?"

He shook his head. "The Harcents and I can talk in here. You go on out."

Jessica watched from the porch as Kevin Lochner followed Timmy into the garden, holding his camera like a woman. She did not want to direct this scene, terrified that she would color it with emotions she could no longer trust. She saw Timmy now through her own eyes, eyes that were filled with tears. Without the protection of her camera, he was real, not an abstraction. She could not intrude.

"I'm not hungry."

"You have to eat," Doug said.

"I would like a drink."

They found a table in a quiet corner of the hotel bar. "You look tired," he said. "You should be happy. Didn't you get what you wanted? I thought you handled the interview very well."

"Handle," she said. "That's exactly the right word."

He looked at her quizzically. "You're in a funny mood."

"I know," Jessica said, holding her drink with both hands.

"It's hard to explain, but something happened to me this afternoon, Doug. Maybe it's been there all along, building up inside without my even knowing it. I've filmed all kinds of pain: victims of poverty, prejudice, injustice. And I wanted the Harcents to be just like them, helpless, beaten, rattling a tin cup. Somewhere in the back of my mind was the horrible wish that Timmy could be a pitiful invalid, a sad little cripple. I thought I would have a more powerful film and you would have a stronger case. I wanted a desperate mother, a vindictive father, a pathetic child. Isn't that terrific?"

"I coach my witnesses, Jess. I tell them what to wear, what to say, how to win the sympathy of a jury. That's part of my job, too. And no, it's not terrific."

"Then why do we do it?"

"Because we're human."

"There's nothing in me right now that feels human," she said. "What will happen to Timmy?"

"The Harcents will testify here first. And come to New York, if it's necessary."

"And after Timmy parades his infirmities in front of a jury, then what? A lifetime struggling to overcome something that should never have happened in the first place."

"We all do that."

"Too much or too little," she said sadly. "Too much love or not enough. Some children with no food, others with a closet full of toys like those grotesque stuffed animals we saw in the store window."

This was not melancholy, or the emotional vacuum that inevitably follows the main event. He saw that she was deeply troubled. "It's never easy," he said. "But that's why we both do what we do. Now come on, cheer up, for Christ's sake. Let's have dinner. Let's get drunk."

"No. I have to pick up the film in the morning. And our flight is at twelve. I just want to go to bed."

They rode up together in the antiquated lift that groaned and rattled its way to their floor. Standing in front of her door, searching for the key in her purse, she asked, "Where are you?"

"Just down the hall. Can I come in for a minute?"

She felt like a woman flirting with disloyalty. But she did not want to be alone.

Arnie Sultan's blood-red roses were on the bureau. Jessica strode angrily across the room. "I told the maid to throw these damn things away!" She picked up the vase and held it at arm's length like something dead, turning in one direction, then another, looking for a place to put it. Suddenly she hurled it against the wall, breaking the vase and scattering the roses over the carpet. Then she began to cry.

Doug put his arms around her. He could feel the shivers, the tiny tremors that shook her body. She rested her head on his shoulder, trying to stop the tears. He drew her down on the bed. "It's okay, Jess. It'll be a fine film."

"It's *always* a fine film. Always! And what good will it do? That boy, that poor little boy . . . "

His hands caressed her back. His face was rough against her cheek, his body hard pressed against hers. The expression in his dark eyes was new to her. For four years she had known only one look, one texture, one manner of touching, and her first impulse was to push him away. She did not want him. But in his arms, in his words, she could lose the memory of Timmy Harcent, lose herself.

Just as he had changed during the days they spent together, an indicter of her profession and then a co-conspirator, so his moods changed with her during the night. But always lingering, always tender, intensity without urgency. He was not interested in the goal of momentary explosion, rather in attenuating minutes. He made her feel innocent, virginal, as she experienced sensations that were completely new, taking, giving, conquering and surrendering time. With him she could relinquish the clock that had been an intrinsic but unconscious part of her lovemaking for years.

Even lying next to him while he slept was strange, different. She turned on her side, feeling the pressure of his back against hers. She saw his clothes thrown carelessly over the back of a chair. He did not have to worry about wrinkles; he did not have to catch a train. No, he was still there, not yet a memory.

He stirred out of sleep, blinking his eyes, picturing the expression on Mel's face when he told him that he had finally found a Person with Standing, the seven-letter smile of congratulations if he knew the rest. Morning light filtered through the white curtains at the windows of the room and he remembered the spectrum of feelings she had aroused in him last night. He had not planned this. When he took her in his arms, he intended to offer only reassurance. Even after they were in bed, he had not meant to stay the night. He had imagined countless times what she would be like. But she was not like that at all. Expecting merely another void, he had experienced instead a fullness, completion. He had dared and she had returned his challenge, reawakening parts of him that had functioned senselessly for years. The pleasure they had discovered in each other was shared and he felt no pride of conquest, no self-satisfaction that he had proved some archaic point. They had made love. The war was over with her, and within himself.

"Jess?" His eyes fully open now, he rolled over, an arm outstretched to embrace her. She wasn't there.

She was sitting at the desk at the far side of the room, fully dressed. "I didn't mean to wake you."

An expression as dark as the color of his eyes came over his face. He propped himself up in bed, drawing the sheet around his waist. "What time is it?"

"After eight."

"I'll order breakfast," he said, running his fingers through his tousled hair. "It's the only meal the English know how to make."

"I'll get something downstairs."

"If you can wait, I'll go with you."

"There isn't time." She reached for the phone and dialed a number. "Kevin? I'm sorry to call you at this hour. It's a wrap and our plane leaves at noon. Can I meet you somewhere to pick up the film? And what about the transcript of the audio? I'd like to start editing on the plane. About nine, then. I'll take a taxi. And thank you, Kevin. For the boy, for everything. I promise to do justice to your pictures."

Doug felt naked and foolish. Swinging his legs over the side of the bed, he reached for his clothes and began to dress while Jessica moved quickly around the room, opening and closing drawers, folding clothes into her suitcase. "Be careful of the broken glass," he reminded her.

She looked at the shattered pieces of the vase and the roses strewn over the water-stained carpet. "I guess I did that."

Didn't she remember what else she had done, what they had done together?

"I'll take care of the bill here," she said. "And the car, unless you want to drive it to the airport?"

"I can take a taxi."

"I'll meet you at the airport then, as soon as I can get there." She picked up her suitcase and threw her raincoat over her arm.

"Jess?"

She turned at the door. "Have I forgotten something?"
"Good morning."

He went back to his own room, showered, shaved, and began to pack. Why was he rushing? He had plenty of time, time for breakfast, for the trip to the airport. She was the one in a hurry. Was it because she was a woman, governed since adolescence by the ticking of some internal clock, her own needs compounded by the demands of her profession? No, that wasn't the Jessica of last night. He remembered her wet eyes, her responsive lips. Full of wonder, waiting for him as he chose the plateaus of each new pleasure, lingering with him until he moved on. He had been touched by her tenderness, fused by her passion. It was as if he had dissected a computer, stripping it away piece by piece, then finding at the core, to his complete surprise, a human heart. But sometime during the night the machine had been reassembled. The other Jessica had reemerged and fled.

What would they talk about on the plane, he wondered? Would they cross the Atlantic with their old armor intact, as if nothing had happened? Perhaps nothing had. They were two different people last night. They had met and made love. And now she was gone.

He finished packing, called for a porter, then picking up his briefcase, glanced around the room to make sure he had left nothing behind. In the hall, on the way to the elevator, he passed her door. If he had to, he could forget whatever traces of himself remained in that room.

FIFTEEN

"*J*essie?"

She opened her eyes slowly, uncertain of where she was, half-expecting to see the white curtains fluttering against the windows of her hotel room in London.

"Are you awake?"

"I am now." She tucked the phone between her ear and the pillow. "What is it, Annie? Don't tell me the film got botched in the lab?"

"No, I checked. It's fine. It'll be out of the soup this afternoon. Sorry I missed you."

"I just dropped off the film and came right home."

"I thought so. Then you didn't see the clipping I left on your desk?"

"I didn't even bother to look at the mail."

"TML had a press conference the day before you flew back."

"On Styralon? Did you film it?"

"No and no again. I wasn't invited. But everybody else in town was there. Bradford Danziger announced a twenty-million-dollar grant to the station. And Lyman, of course, made obsequious little noises about how it's men like Danziger and companies like TML that keep American television from being totally buried under a pile of Philistine drivel. Scott and Maureen have been strutting around here like they own the earth. Did Arnie Sultan tell you anything about the grant when you had lunch?"

Jessica sat up, propping herself against the pillows. "Indirectly, I suppose he did. But I thought it was just another smokescreen. I should have known better. Was Ben at the press conference?"

"No, he's been in Washington. He gets back this afternoon. I'm sorry I woke you, but I thought you'd want to know."

"You're right. Now things are beginning to make sense. Like your mystery caller at the library. And last night my doorman told me that two men, who claimed they were from the phone company, tried to get into my apartment while I was away. Can you believe it? The phone company. TML was looking for something."

"It's getting a little thick, Jessie," Ann said.

"It's happened before. The important thing is to finish the film."

"Jeff will be ready to screen the London footage as soon as it's out of the lab."

"Okay, tell him I'll be in this afternoon."

"I can't wait to see it," Ann said. "How was the boy?"

"Not quite what I expected."

"And Doug Weber?"

"Not what I expected either."

Jessica couldn't go back to sleep. Time was more important than ever now. There were only three weeks to air, but she had cut films in less time than that. It was inconceivable that TML had come up with twenty million just to stop her investigation. Not even Danziger could afford that much persuasion. But it seemed clear that he and Lyman Ellis had formed some kind of coalition, a mutuality of interest, that in a strange way had nothing—and everything—to do with her film.

She made coffee and, sitting at the kitchen table, continued work on the transcript of the Harcent interview. Frowning, she recalled how she had used it as a shield on the flight back to New York. Doug read and reread the depositions and briefs prepared by the London lawyers. They scarcely exchanged a word. Nothing was said about what had happened the night before. And at first she was apprehensive, then puzzled, finally grateful. She wanted to forget it, forget the dark mood that Doug had helped her obliterate, deny the alarming depth of feeling he had aroused in her. She wanted to forget him.

Just back from Washington, he looked for Jessica in her office. "She's with Jeff, screening London," Ann told him. "Ask her to call me," he said. "I'll be working late."

Ben returned to his own office. It was Thursday, usually the climax of his week: four days of symbolic anticipation —exchanging glances, touching shoulders, discerning innuendos in her most ordinary gesture, all leading to the moment he arrived at her door, primed for love. But this week she had been in London, depriving him of those moments of furtive foreplay, and as he sorted out the pile of papers on his desk, stuffing some of them in his attaché case to read later on the train, he could think only of her. Each time she went on a trip, he missed her more and more. Thursday nights were not enough, and wondering what it would be like to live with Jessica, he imagined a week in which every day held the heady expectancy that filled him now.

The phone rang and he picked it up, expecting to hear her voice. "Ben? I'd like to talk to you. Are you free?"

"I have a train to catch, Lyman."

"Take the next one. I'll be waiting for you in my office."

Ben felt a dull ache behind his eyes. This was not an idle encounter in the men's room. It was a summons to the imperial inner sanctum. Their last talk had left him drained, soiled; this one might cost even more.

Lyman usually greeted visitors seated behind his desk. When Ben entered his office, he was standing, but he quickly gestured Ben to a low couch where he could retain the advantage. "You drink Scotch, don't you? Water or soda?"

"Straight, please."

Lyman went to the bar to pour their drinks, and Ben noticed that he filled his own glass only with soda. "I've been looking at the figures for your department, Ben. You're way over budget, and Jessica seems to be the prime offender. How much did she spend on her trip to London?"

"She hasn't submitted her expenses yet," Ben said warily. "But she hasn't been wasting money, and I thought the trip warranted the cost. Is that what's really bothering you?"

Lyman handed Ben his drink. "Money is always a concern. But frankly, there is something else. I'm told she filmed a family in London that's planning to sue because of the damage they claim this drug did to their child. According to my sources, there's no truth to their allegations. They are total fabrications. I suspect Jessica has been taken in by a hungry lawyer."

Ben had promised himself he would not give in to his anger as he had the last time. "I can't comment on the London footage, Lyman. I haven't seen it. But you can tell your sources that the lawyer involved happens to be a member of one of the finest public interest firms in the city."

"From what you've seen of the film," Lyman said, still standing, toying with his glass, "can you assure me that Jessica has presented both sides of this issue fairly? There are, as you know, certain standards of journalistic integrity that we must maintain."

"Jessica's integrity is above reproach," Ben said, still controlling his temper.

"Her air date is only three weeks away. Is she going to make it?"

"Of course. She's in editing right now. It's a good film, Lyman. She's built a powerful case against the drug. Is that what's worrying your friend Danziger?"

Lyman finally sat, crossing his legs and leaning forward in his chair in an attitude of confidence and intimacy. "It's too soon, Ben."

"Too soon for what?"

"Too soon after the TML grant to air the film. We would be rubbing Danziger's nose in his own generosity."

"You know damn well his money didn't pay for her film."

"Of course I do. But I'm thinking of the impression it will create, not only on Danziger but on every other corporation that supports this station."

"Has Danziger threatened to hold up the grant?"

"Certainly not. But the agreement is still with the lawyers and he may well ask for certain conditions and qualifications. Don't you see, Ben, it's not just Jessica's film or the

TML grant? It's all the films, all the grants. While I respect your loyalty to Jessica and your documentary unit, it is a rather shortsighted and narrow view. *I* have a station to run."

Ben made a gesture of exasperation. "What are you worried about, Lyman? Danziger can't back out now without explaining why. And that kind of publicity would be as bad for his company's image as a flap about Styralon. You've got him just where you want him."

"You're right," Lyman replied coolly. "I've got his name on the dotted line and that's precisely where I intend to keep it. Perhaps you forget that I talked Danziger into making an 'unrestricted' grant to the station. That means more money for every department, including yours. Money you can use to keep your documentary unit alive."

It had taken a little time, Ben thought, but Lyman had finally zeroed in on his target, using the same weapon Danziger had used on him. Money. He gulped down what was left of his drink.

"If you'd like another, help yourself," Lyman said with a flicker of satisfaction in his smile.

Ben got up, went to the bar, and with his back to Lyman, filled his glass to the top. Spinning around, he could no longer control his indignation. "I see what's coming. It isn't worth it, not to me. A documentary unit that can't expose a lie or reveal a truth doesn't have any reason to exist. You may think Danziger's money is our salvation. I say if we knuckle under to him now, we're damned. I won't kill Jessica's film. I won't have any part of it. It's worse than censorship. It's self-destruction."

"Grow up, Ben," Lyman said wearily. "I'm not asking you to do anything. It's already been done. I've simply rearranged the documentary schedule. We'll use reruns for the rest of the summer. And Jessica's film can be aired any time you like, this fall, as part of a completely new series. By that time, we'll have the grant and everyone will have forgotten about it."

"Not with Arnie Sultan grinding out a story a day about TML's generosity."

"That'll die down eventually, I assure you. And Jessica's film will get a better rating after Labor Day than in the middle of the summer. I'm sure she would be the first to appreciate that."

Lyman's interest in ratings for a documentary, especially for a film produced by Jessica Lenhart, was so perverse, so fraudulent, that Ben almost laughed. "There's one thing you've forgotten, Lyman," he said, frustration entering his voice. "Her film is timed to an event. The case against the drug is ready to go to court."

"I doubt it. Not in the middle of the summer. No, I've thought this problem through very carefully, Ben, and I've arrived at the solution that should satisfy everyone, including you."

"And what if Styralon really is dangerous?" Ben said, slamming his drink down on the bar. "Have you thought that through?"

"That's Danziger's concern," Lyman said, dismissing Ben with a wave of his hand. "I think that's all. I wouldn't want you to miss your train."

Impatient, worried about the TML grant, filled with excitement after screening the London footage, Jessica waited in the lobby for Ben, while the security guard seated behind a high counter leafed idly through a newspaper. Then she saw him: attaché case swinging from his arm, blue blazer thrown over his shoulder, collar unbuttoned, tie loosened. He looked more than tired. He looked defeated.

"Sorry I'm late," he said. "Another little session with

Lyman." He kissed her on the forehead, catching her by surprise. He was usually so cautious about a public embrace. The security guard did not look up from his paper.

Outside the sky was growing dark in a slow, purple summer way, and the heat of the city hit them like a wall. Dry dusty air blew through the lowered windows of the cab that took them downtown.

"I can't believe it's summer," Jessica said. "It happens on every film, losing a season."

"You look pale, Jess. You're working too hard."

Because it was so late, they decided to have dinner first—like the kiss in the lobby, another deviation from their Thursday night routine. In the dim light of the restaurant, she noticed that shadows clouded his eyes, and when he spoke, it was with forced cheerfulness. "Tell me about London, Jess," he said. "I want to hear everything from airport to airport."

Trying to lift him out of his gloom, she colored her description of the trip with the hues and scents of the city, told him of the unordered limousine, Arnie Sultan's roses, Kevin Lochner's love affair with his camera, hoping he wouldn't notice that something was missing.

"And the boy?"

His question was inevitable. "He was just a little boy," she said softly, "who wants to be like other boys."

"Then it's a wrap," he said with a strange lack of enthusiasm. "Have you got everything you need?"

"Everything except Bowen. But I can run the depositions from the English doctors on a crawl. Styralon *is* a teratogen, Ben. Doug thinks his case is airtight. But I'm worried."

"About what?"

"TML. I didn't know about the grant. It explains everything: the calls to the library checking up on Ann, the two men who said they were from the telephone company and tried to get into my apartment, Arnie Sultan's limousine and roses."

"That's sixties stuff, Jess. I don't think TML would try anything like that, no matter how unhappy they are."

"Arnie Sultan *is* the sixties. He's getting information from someone and that someone has to be Lyman. Was your meeting about my film? I can tell you're worried, too. It's in your eyes. What's going on?"

"Something is always going on with Lyman," he answered wearily. "And yes, we did talk about your film, but only indirectly. Whatever we may think about TML, the grant is good news for the station, Jess. We'll get a chunk of it, enough for a new documentary series next year. And your film will lead off the fall season."

She wasn't certain how to react. Her thoughts raced ahead of her words. "What's happening to my film, Ben? You *can't* delay it. Doug will be in court in a few weeks. It'll be too late."

"The city is closed in August, Jess. You know that. Look at it this way. You'll have more time. Maybe you can get to Bowen and really do a job on McCampbell. And you'll catch a bigger audience in the fall."

"Was this Lyman's idea?"

"It wasn't anybody's idea. And it's not just your film. The whole schedule is being shuffled around. Now come on, let's not spoil our evening. It's okay, Jess. I can handle it. It's part of my job. Trust me."

"It's Lyman I don't trust."

Walking back to her apartment with only an hour or so left before Ben had to catch his train, Jessica felt there was something askew about the entire evening. She wondered if the familiar rituals would have reassured her that nothing had changed, that her night with Doug had been only a momentary transgression.

Her doorman handed her the mail and a huge cardboard box. Ben's roses. "So many?" she exclaimed, when she opened the box in her apartment.

"I wanted your homecoming to be special."

In bed, folding her in his arms, he said, "Remember the Ritz." But part of her memory was elsewhere, and the way he made love was familiar only in its haste, its urgency. Unable to share his intensity, she found herself in a role she had never played with him before. The observer, directing in her imagination a film of their lovemaking, in slow motion, prolonging and attenuating the moments of tenderness, allowing the caresses to linger, expanding time.

"I love you, Jess. You know that," he whispered. "And you know if Sara were . . . "

She placed her hand on his lips, silencing him. He kissed her and then he was in the shower. She picked up his watch and wedding ring from the living room, straightened the knot of his tie as he stood in the hallway. "Let's have lunch tomorrow," he said. "I want to see the London footage. And I want you to get this conspiracy business out of your mind. Lyman is Lyman. Don't worry about it."

He picked up his attaché case, kissed her, and hurried out of her apartment.

She turned the lock and leaned against the door. No, this time it wasn't the Ritz. But why did it have to be? In the album of their four years together, why did she have to paste the same pictures on every page? Theirs was a love, not a liaison, but love changes, grows. And tonight, for the first time, she had wanted something different, something more. Yet when her goal flashed momentarily into sight, she had drawn back, taking cover in familiar ground. She was tired. Her thoughts were confused. And she wished she could replay the evening, edit out her concern about the film, her fears about Lyman. With better light, the shadows that lined Ben's face would disappear.

Her mail was lying on the hall table next to the empty box that had held Ben's roses. Bills, circulars, magazines, and an envelope addressed to her in an unfamiliar hand. The postmark was Los Angeles. She tore it open.

My dear Miss Lenhart,

Although we have not met, Bertha and I have talked of little else since you left Los Angeles, and nothing else since you sent the transcript of the interviews in your film and the news of the child in London. I have been in touch with my friends there and they are optimistic about stopping the drug. I am less optimistic. I know Karl Engle. I have worked with the people at McCampbell. And sadly, I am all too familiar with the cumbersome bureaucracy of the FDA. Bertha told you that I believed there was nothing more I could do. Now I know there is. We are coming to New York next week and will try to reach you as soon as we arrive.

Cordially,

Daniel Bowen

She started for the phone and then realized it was too late to call Doug. Her confused mood of a few moments ago disappeared. She could see everything clearly now. Lyman Ellis had hung like a black cloud over every film she had ever made, threatening to temper the truth in the name of journalistic fair play, soften its bite in the name of editorial prudence. He would use the same arguments this time to disguise his real concern: placating TML and sewing up his precious grant. But the postponement had given her more time to finish her work. With Daniel Bowen, all the pieces would fall into place. And with Ben as her ally, she would have her film edited, written, mixed, and ready for air, a film not even Lyman Ellis could stop.

 *SIXTEEN* ∽

*D*espite the warmth of his greeting, Jessica saw the worried expression on Paul's face, just as she had heard the hard edge in Kate's voice a few hours before when she commanded her to come to the apartment. "When?" Jessica asked. "Now," Kate said. "I can't," Jessica protested. "You have to." The phone clicked off and Kate was gone. Jessica had planned to spend the evening constructing the questions she would ask Daniel Bowen. He and his wife were in New York and he had called her from their hotel. She still had hours of work ahead of her to prepare for the interview which was set for the next day. But something in Kate's tone told her this was not an idle invitation.

"Wine or coffee, my dear?" Paul asked, guiding her to the living room where Kate was waiting.

"Coffee, please. I have to work tonight. Daniel Bowen is here. And he's agreed to talk to me. I'm very grateful, Paul. I couldn't have found him without you."

"So, Dr. Bowen has reappeared," Paul said. "That may explain it."

"Explain what?" Jessica asked.

"You tell her, Kate. I'll get the coffee."

"Sit down, Jessica, please. This won't take long."

"Is it about Ben?"

"I'm afraid it is, at least indirectly. There's something you should know, and I suppose I'd better start at the beginning. A week or so ago, I got a call from a man who said he was a friend of Paul's. He told me he was writing an article about how people's neuroses affect them in their professional lives and Paul had suggested that he interview me. I said no, at first. I didn't have time. But he rattled off his credentials and when he gave me the name of the magazine, it all sounded perfectly legitimate. And he was very insistent. So I agreed to talk to him."

Paul returned to the room, carrying a tray with mugs of coffee. "Without checking with me, I might add."

"I admit that was stupid," Kate said. "But you were in Paris."

"And your friend knew it. A Mr. Parker, wasn't it?"

"David Parker."

Paul shook his head. "Such an innocuous, unimaginative name."

"He was an innocuous man. Young, well dressed, moderately intelligent. He started by asking me about doctors and lawyers and how I thought their personal conflicts influenced the kind of medicine and law they practiced. Then he began talking about journalists. Was it possible that someone with a personality disorder would constantly pick themes for his work that were anti-establishment, critical, or muckraking? A little alarm bell went off in my head when he asked me that, Jessica. After all, Paul is a journalist and it occurred to me that David Parker was snooping about him."

"A brilliant deduction," Paul said. "Did you answer the question with me in mind?"

"I told him it could work both ways. Such a person might be anti-establishment or slavishly conventional and rage internally. It's not predictable. I thought that would be the end of it. But then Mr. Parker launched into the subject of sex. Could unconventional sexual preferences influence a journalist's attitudes and ideas? I bristled at that, certain now that Mr. Parker had come to find out some dark secret in Paul's life. Or tell me about one."

"You should have known better, my darling. I have no dark secrets. Just one or two very pale ones."

"I was torn between anger and curiosity," Kate continued. "So I told Mr. Parker again that it was impossible to generalize about such a question and asked if he had anyone particular in mind. That ended the interview. He thanked me and left. I called Paul in Paris immediately and, of course, he had never heard of Mr. Parker."

"Still, I wasn't surprised," Paul said. "A lot of people have been trying to nail me with something for years. The surprising thing was that David Parker had come to see my wife. A daring stroke, or so I thought."

Jessica sipped her coffee, amused by the story, but puzzled by why Kate and Paul were so insistent about telling it to her now. "Did you ever find out who he was?"

"Not yet," Paul said. "But that isn't the end of it. I flew back from Paris last week and Kate and I spent the weekend in Connecticut with friends. The apartment was broken into while we were away."

"We both assumed," Kate said, "that Mr. Parker had returned to look for something to use against Paul. We were wrong, Jessica. The only thing missing was your file."

Startled, Jessica almost spilled her mug of coffee. "My file? I don't understand. How did they know I even had one? What were they trying to find out?"

Paul's expression was solemn. "Why don't you tell us who *they* are?" he asked.

"TML or McCampbell," Jessica said angrily. "They tried to get into my apartment, too."

"Styralon," Paul said. "I told you, my dear. I figured it out immediately. Our little Jessica has opened up another can of worms."

"But how could they dare take such an enormous risk?"

"There's one obvious answer to that," Paul said. "Money. They think the drug is worth millions. But there's another not quite so obvious reason. Knowing you, I suspect your film is about more than the drug. It's about the system, the links, the connections, the way these companies operate. Styralon isn't really all that important, Jessica, not to them. The drug can be altered to make it safer, minimize the risks, eliminate the side effects."

"Side effects?" Jessica interrupted. "Stunted bodies, hearts that pump foul blood. We're not speaking of a headache, Paul."

"I know that. And to us it's terrible. A crime. But to them it's simply a small error in judgment that can be fixed. Warnings can be issued to the doctors who prescribe the drug. And if all else fails, it can be withdrawn from the market. Then it becomes a writeoff, including the lawsuits they may have to settle in or out of court. No, there's nothing new in blowing the whistle on bad drugs. The companies that make them can handle that. It's the story behind these drugs, how they happen, and why they will continue to happen. That's what they want to conceal. And that's what Mr. Parker was all about."

"I can't believe it," Jessica said.

"You *are* a lamb in a den of wolves, my pet," Paul said. "This is only the beginning, I assure you. They're running scared. And I suspect Daniel Bowen is the reason. Somehow they were able to keep him quiet until you came along, and they were willing to humor you for a while, throw up the usual small obstructions. Now they want to get you off the story."

"My file?"

"Exactly. Blackmail. If they can find out something *you* want to conceal, something more important to you than the film, it would be a tradeoff."

"But what?"

"Ben," Kate said, extending her hands in the gesture of resignation that Jessica had seen so many times before. "They were probably looking for a case history, alcohol, drugs, some psychological or sexual problem. They found Ben."

"She had to tell me," Paul said. "But you mustn't be too hard on yourself, my dear Kate. If Mr. Parker knew where to look, he probably had some idea of what he was looking for. You can't imagine your affair with Ben is a secret. Not after all these years. Someone at the station must know about it."

Jessica was stunned. "You mean they would threaten Ben and me?"

"They already have," Paul said with a shrug. "They know that you know that they know. Et cetera, et cetera. It's classic in its simplicity. But there's an easy way to beat it. You must keep all of this to yourself. Act innocent, as if nothing has happened or else you'll play right into their hands."

"But I have to tell Ben."

"Above all, do *not* tell Ben. Don't you understand their little game? First of all, they hope you'll back away from the film to protect him. Or that he may feel he has to kill the film to protect you."

"I've been harassed before," Jessica said flatly. "We thrive on it."

"This *kind* of harassment? You forget, my dear Jessica, that it's directed at him, too. I've known Ben for years, and no one questions his journalistic integrity. But he's a man . . . "

"A man who loves me," Jessica interrupted.

"A man with a reputation, a job, a wife and children," Kate added acidly. "He would have that to think about, too."

"Ben and I will survive."

"Perhaps," Paul said with kindness, not criticism, in his voice. "But is all this protection really necessary? Tell Ben *after* your film has aired. Now let me get you some fresh coffee. Or would you like to stay for dinner? I'm sure we could prevail upon Kate to cook something authentically and unmistakably American."

Jessica smiled in spite of herself. "No, thanks. I have to get ready for Bowen. I'm going to finish this film."

"That's my girl," Paul said. "But promise me one thing. Next time, take on the Mafia. Much less wear and tear than a multinational corporation."

They met in the glass-enclosed garden of a restaurant near her apartment. The floor was paved with red brick, the walls hung with baskets of brightly colored flowers. Cheerful waitresses wore crisp white aprons around their waists. The menu was elaborate and expensive. "It's a long way from the Casa Mendoza," Doug said. "Christ, doesn't that seem a hundred years ago."

They had not seen each other since their return from London. Jessica had called to tell Doug about the TML grant and the postponement of her air date. He had called her to say he had finally obtained the documents he wanted from the FDA. When she called again to report that the Bowens were coming to New York, he had asked her to dinner. She refused, using work as an excuse. She could not risk another evening alone with him. And now she could sense the sarcasm in his voice, hear the reproach that she was treating him as nothing more than an accomplice in making her film, an accessory. But for her, the night in London had been an end, not a beginning. She had to keep him at a distance.

Waiting for the Bowens to arrive, she told him about David Parker and the stolen file. But she spoke of it lightly, humorously, disguising her genuine concern, just as she had hidden her suspicion that the new air date for her film was somehow linked to the TML grant.

Doug didn't think it was very funny. "First limousines and roses, and now burglary. Was there anything in the file they can use against you?"

She had anticipated that question. "I hope not. My father died. We talked about loss." And magic circles and white lights, she thought. "I wonder what they'll try to do to you?"

"They've got five-hundred-dollar-an-hour lawyers to deal with me. You're different, you're television, the real threat, especially now that Bowen has come out of hiding. What line are you going to take with him?"

The memory of Timmy Harcent flashed through her mind, along with her grim wish that he could have been more pathetic. She would not make that mistake again, casting Daniel Bowen in some preconceived role, a sick, old man on the verge of madness, just to serve her own purpose. No, she would not make that mistake again.

Her living room was filled with lights, electric cords snaking across the rug. Dan Spignole had already set up his camera and his greeting, deferential and obsequious, was as annoying as his usual hostility. The crew remembered Doug from the Barwick interview and shook hands politely with Bertha and Daniel Bowen.

At the last moment, Jessica had switched the site of the interview, instructing the crew to set up in her apartment while she and Doug had lunch with the Bowens. There she would be safe from snooping eyes and station gossips, and if Dr. Bowen was in fragile health, or in a distressed mental state, he would be more comfortable in her apartment than in a sterile film studio. He was a tall, wiry man with a shock of white hair falling over a broad forehead. When he and his wife had entered the restaurant, Jessica was struck by their similarity, as if their years together had worn away even the physical differences between them. But it was evident which of them possessed the greater strength. Bertha Bowen was as Jessica remembered, dignified, self-assured, the dark circles that lined her eyes fainter now. But her husband seemed to exist only in one dimension. His eyes were gray and without light. During their conversation at lunch, even when his words were kind, he didn't smile. And when bitter words came from his mouth, his expression did not change. Nor did his voice. He was a monotone of a man. But not ill, not mad.

The intention of the lunch was to reassure Dr. Bowen and establish some personal connection before the interview. But Jessica felt she had been only partially successful. He was so vague, so tentative, she feared that after all the weeks of waiting, he would, in the end, reveal nothing. Once they reached her apartment, however, he seemed to feel much more at ease. He expressed an interest in the camera and Spignole demonstrated some of its sophisticated lenses. His conversation with the other members of the crew was technical, and Jessica saw the curiosity and intelligence that must have guided him in his own work. If only she could capture that on camera, not his lusterless eyes, his vacant, unvarying expression.

Preparing for the interview, she checked the arrangements the crew had made, turned off the air conditioner and raised the windows, preferring the bleating of a horn or the wail of a siren from the street to the low persistent drone of the machine. She noticed that Doug was making an unobtrusive inspection of his own, studying the pictures on the walls, examining the titles of the books on the shelves, like a detective searching for clues to a crime. Nothing escaped his attention, even the odd asceticism of her one-slice toaster. At lunch he had been quiet, almost sullen, and Jessica found it unsettling that she had the power to provoke such displeasure. Perhaps he respected the distance she had re-created between them, but here, investigating the details of her life, he made her feel as a woman feels when a man undresses her with his eyes.

"What's with the flowers, Jess?" Spignole asked. "It looks like someone died in here. About a week ago. They're going to be in the shot."

They were Ben's roses, forgotten since last Thursday night. Jessica picked up the vase from the coffee table, aware that Doug was watching her. He feigned a gesture, as if ducking out of her line of fire. She acknowledged the memory with a half smile, carried the vase to the kitchen, and dumped the roses in the trash.

Just before the interview began, Bertha Bowen straightened her husband's jacket and tried to smooth the unruly shock of white hair over his forehead. Then she sat next to Doug, leaning forward in her chair, cupping her chin in her hand, offering silent support from across the room.

"Rolling, Jess. Profile of a Miracle, Dr. Bowen, Take One. Speed."

"Dr. Bowen, would you tell me how you first became involved with Styralon?"

He looked alarmed, glancing first at his wife and then at Jessica. "Is that what you're calling this film, Miss Lenhart, 'Profile of a Miracle'?"

"Cut," Jessica said. "I'm sorry, Dr. Bowen, I should have explained. That's just a working title. It's called 'Defects of the Heart.' Now may we begin again?"

"Ready, Jess. You've got speed. Bowen, Take Two."

Drawing himself up, but still speaking in a monotone, Dr. Bowen described his work on Styralon. "It's a synthetic hormone, and I had been employed by Chanterelle Laboratories for many years to conduct tests of similar drugs."

"Were you aware that Styralon was manufactured by McCampbell?"

"Yes. The test samples were supplied by McCampbell. I was also aware that the drug was already being used in England, where reports indicated it was a safe and effective means of preventing spontaneous abortion. But I could take nothing for granted with a drug of such enormous chemical complexity, especially one that would be given to pregnant women. I studied the English tests very carefully, but I also conducted a wide range of tests of my own."

"Could you describe the nature of those tests?"

"Essentially, they were divided into two phases, the first to study the effect of the drug on the mother, and the second to study its effect on the developing fetus."

"I assume these tests were performed on laboratory animals."

"Certainly. Human testing would be quite impossible. But there the reports from England were encouraging. The Committee on the Safety of Medicines, the English equivalent of our Food and Drug Administration, had approved the drug and it had been in use for more than five years with apparent safety."

"What were the results of your tests, Dr. Bowen?"

"The drug, while not invariably successful in preventing miscarriage, had no adverse side effects on the mother."

"And on the fetus?"

"I was not permitted to complete all those tests."

Jessica circled her fist for a close-up. "Would you explain why?"

Daniel Bowen turned his face away from the camera, his shoulders sagged, and he seemed to have trouble catching his breath. His wife went quickly to his side. He took her hand. "I'm sorry, Miss Lenhart. Perhaps Bertha can tell you this part of the story."

"No, Daniel," she said firmly. "You must tell it. You've kept it inside for too long."

The only sound in the room was the low murmur of the camera. No one spoke, waiting for Dr. Bowen to continue.

"Our son was gravely ill," he said finally, his voice barely audible.

Jessica had promised herself she would not mention Peter Bowen; she intended to stay on the subject of Styralon without complicating the story with the Bowens' personal anguish over the death of their son. They could be spared the pain of reliving that. But now she realized Dr. Bowen's grief was as much a part of the story as the Harcents' courage.

"Our son was in England," he continued. "He could not

be moved, and throughout the months I was working on Styralon, Bertha and I traveled back and forth as often as we could. Finally, Bertha stayed on, and then there came a time when I realized I had to be with Peter, too. I asked Chanterelle for a leave of absence. There was still much more to be done on Styralon, but I was assured the testing would continue and that I could resume my work when I returned. I went to England, but it was too late. There was nothing we could do for Peter."

As Dr. Bowen spoke, traces of emotion began to show on his face and his eyes glistened with tears. "He was a golden boy. And a remarkable young man. He had lived under the shadow of his illness for years, and knowing it was terminal, he volunteered to submit to experimental forms of treatment. I was proud of him, or so I said, but deep within me, I was horrified. My son, a laboratory animal. I knew of the possible dangers, the certain pain. There was no chance of saving his own life, hope only that these new medications would some day help others. And as I watched him suffer, I was filled with a suffering of my own. I had devoted my life to a science that was killing my son. Perhaps he sensed that, for in the end, when his pain became unendurable, Peter took his own life."

Dr. Bowen drew a deep breath. "Forgive me. That's not the story I meant to tell. But during Peter's illness and after his death, Styralon was the furthest thing from my mind, until colleagues in England who knew of my work told me there were new reports of teratogenic side effects, unconfirmed but disturbing enough to be of concern. Bertha and I returned to America, and I went to Chanterelle, expecting to continue my tests on the drug."

"You said earlier you hadn't completed your tests on the fetus," Jessica remarked.

"That's right."

"Did *any* of your tests indicate that the drug was a teratogen?"

"Some of them," Dr. Bowen began slowly. "But they were inconclusive. That's why the English reports were so disturbing, and I was anxious to continue my own tests. But when I went back to Chanterelle, I was told that all the testing has been completed."

"Who told you that?"

"The head of the laboratory, Dr. Karl Engle. I didn't think it possible. I had been away only a few months. Dr. Engle was aware of the new reports from England, but he said his own tests proved to his satisfaction that Styralon was not a teratogen."

"And that's when you retired from Chanterelle?"

"No, there was no talk of retirement. Not then. I was assigned to begin tests of another drug. But first I went to McCampbell and met with Dr. Alton Medford, the head of Research and Development there. He, too, was aware of the new English reports, but he said that Chanterelle's tests, as well as tests he had conducted, convinced him the drug was safe. In fact, all the results had been submitted to the government and the first phase of the approval process was already under way. He assured me, however, that if any further tests proved unfavorable, the information would be submitted to the FDA as the law requires."

"So you went back to work for Chanterelle," Jessica said.

"No, that proved to be impossible. Dr. Engle was furious at me for going to McCampbell. He accused me of disloyalty and endangering the reputation of his laboratory. He said my work on Styralon had been slipshod and called me a troublemaker. He even suggested that my son's death had caused some kind of mental derangement. I couldn't believe the way he spoke to me."

"And Dr. Engle fired you?"

"No. He said I was too ill to continue working and asked me to retire. That way I would have my pension and benefits. There was no alternative. Peter's illness had drained our savings."

"Did you perhaps think your pension was a kind of bribe to ensure your silence?"

"I didn't know what to think. My mind was in total confusion. But I couldn't remain silent. Bertha and I went back to England, and in collaboration with friends there, I wrote an article about Styralon. It was not intended for a medical journal; I merely cited Styralon as an example of the way American companies rush drugs to the market without taking the proper precautions. The article was accepted for publication, but a few weeks later, I received a letter from the editor of the magazine, informing me that it could not be published after all. He thanked me and enclosed a small honorarium. I'm told in publishing it's called a 'kill fee.' "

"Do you think McCampbell or Chanterelle were responsible?"

"I didn't know. But soon after, I received a notice from Chanterelle. It seems I was no longer qualified to receive a pension. And the payments were stopped."

"One minute," Spignole called out.

"I know how difficult this must be for you, Dr. Bowen," Jessica said. "Let's take a break while they reload the camera. May I get you something to drink?"

Doug joined Jessica in the kitchen as she filled a pitcher with ice water. "It's incredible," he whispered. "They all knew. McCampbell. Chanterelle. Collusion, fraud, even perjury. We've got them, Jess. If you can find out where the government fits into all this, that's the last link."

She couldn't share his enthusiasm. She had what she wanted, but her thoughts were only of Dr. Bowen and the ordeal she was asking him to relive in front of her grinding camera. Opening carefully sealed doors, inflaming old wounds—how long had she done it without seeing that she caused pain, inflicted injuries of her own?

"We're ready, Jess," Spignole called out.

"Portrait of a Miracle, Dr. Bowen, Roll Fifty-nine, Take Three. Speed."

At the crack of the slate, Jessica was about to ask a question of Dr. Bowen, but he began to speak immediately, the words pouring out of him now. "Bertha and I moved to California. My wife has relatives there who we knew could help us. Still, I was haunted by Styralon. I had nightmares. I couldn't sleep. But there seemed nothing more I could do until Bertha suggested I go directly to the government. It was a very slim chance, I thought. I was no longer employed. I represented no group. I had no official standing. But I went to Washington and met with the woman at the FDA who had received McCampbell's application for approval—Mrs. Barwick. She was very kind, very professional. I told her of my fears that the drug had not been adequately tested and she seemed surprised. She said my signature was on all of the reports and none of them were unfavorable to the drug."

Dr. Bowen reached for a glass of water. "I was outraged and I'm afraid I lost my temper," he said. And for the first time an expression of amusement crossed his face. "I'm sure I frightened the poor woman. She probably thought I was mad. She asked me what definite proof I had that the drug was a teratogen, and I was forced to say I had none. But I handed her the reports I had received from my colleagues in England. I also gave her a summary of my own preliminary tests. It was highly irregular, she said, but she agreed to pass this information on to her superiors."

"Was that material sent?"

"Yes."

"But, Dr. Bowen, we were told at the agency that no

reports unfavorable to Styralon had been received from any source."

"Then someone is lying," he said.

For a brief moment, it occurred to Jessica that it might be Dr. Bowen himself. Perhaps his work on Styralon had been slipshod and incomplete, and his story merely a belated act of personal vindication. "Did you do anything further?"

"I thought I had done what I could. At the very least, the FDA would require further tests. I returned to California with an enormous burden lifted from my mind. I wanted to work again. But I couldn't find a job."

"Were you given any reason?"

"Oh, many reasons. I was too old, unfamiliar with the new technology. But my years at Chanterelle were well known and I suspect Karl Engle was the real reason. Finally, I stopped looking. And when I read that Styralon had been approved, I gave up in total defeat. They had won."

"In your opinion, Dr. Bowen, is Styralon a dangerous drug?"

"Yes. I'm completely convinced of that. The evidence cannot be ignored."

"Could you describe the nature of that evidence?"

"That's painful, even for me. I saw an infant in an English hospital whose mother had taken the drug. He was born without arms and legs and did not survive. Styralon is a hard teratogen."

Difficult as it was, Jessica had to ask the next question. "Then it could be argued, Dr. Bowen, that you shouldn't have remained silent, that there was more you could have done."

"Yes, I suppose there was. The newspapers? Someone higher at FDA? But Bertha and I had been through so much and I knew what was being said about me. I suspect that even you, Miss Lenhart, may question my story. I don't blame you. As a scientist I know that even the best evidence, placed under the magnifying glass of personal motivation, can be distorted. So I kept silent. And when Styralon was approved, I found I could no longer believe in the integrity of my profession or of the government. I could no longer believe in myself."

"And now?" Jessica asked.

"Bertha has made me see that I was destroying whatever time there is left for us. I'm still not sure what can be saved. Not Peter. Not my work or my reputation. All that is lost. But Styralon must be stopped."

Spignole's voice broke through the silence that followed Dr. Bowen's last words. "Runout, Jess. Do you want to reload?"

"No, that's all," she said, for once grateful for his gruff interruption.

Bertha Bowen went to her husband's side, sitting with him in wordless communication. And Jessica felt that this time, perhaps, her poking and prodding, her reawakening of injury and pain, might at least bring some peace to their lives.

"Okay, that's a wrap," Spignole said. "Let's turn on the air conditioner. You can't breathe in here."

∾ SEVENTEEN ∾

A moving collage of faces flickered across the screen; a steady stream of words poured from the speaker of the Moviola. Using the transcripts and the footage counter on the machine as a guide, Jessica spent a week in the editing room, selecting scenes from each of the interviews, and Jeff strung them together into an Assembly—a long and uncreative arrangement of the material. When they completed their last cut, Jessica, examining the counter, let her head fall into her hands, despairing. "Damn. Three hours. Now we have to make it work."

The next week was spent culling from those three hours

the scenes that waned in importance after countless view-ings. But at the end of the first day, they had edited out only twenty minutes. So they did it again. And again, until finally they had a rough cut and Jessica, afraid to look at the counter herself, asked wearily, "How long is it now?"

"Still an epic," Jeff said. "An hour and forty-eight min-utes. We've got to get almost an hour out of it somewhere."

At this point, much of the material that had survived the initial cuts seemed essential, and when Jeff snipped scenes she was accustomed to seeing, it felt like an amputation. "Don't fall in love with anything this early," he warned. "A week from now, you'll never miss it." He said that every time, on every film, and she knew he would say it. But she was inconsolable with each new cut and gave up only after a battle.

Neither of them had much else of a life. Newspapers, phone calls from friends, were all intolerable intrusions, and Jessica would collapse on her bed at night, sometimes falling asleep in her clothes. Ann hovered around the editing room, bringing coffee and sandwiches, or racing back and forth to the library to look for some odd piece of information. Late one afternoon, she handed Jessica a medical magazine. "Page thirty-four," she said without further comment.

Jessica flipped the magazine open to a slick double-page spread advertising Styralon: the same fleecy clouds floating on a sky of blue, the same smiling faces of pregnant women, the same raspberry-cheeked baby cradled in a mother's arms, the same glowing copy she had read on the McCamp-bell circular. She called Doug.

"I know, I've seen it. It's in all the magazines."

"But that means they're starting to sell it. Can't you do something?"

"I'm on the calendar in Federal District Court, asking for a temporary restraining order. But McCampell is flooding the courts with documents attesting to the safety of Styralon. Your film is crucial now, Jess. When can I see it?"

"I'll let you know."

Toward the end of the second week, she and Jeff had just screened an hour-and-fifteen-minute rough cut when he asked, "What do you want to do with these? They're slated Dr. Millicent Rogers. Three rolls of her."

"She's just the shill from McCampbell that Arnie Sultan provided. A corporate stooge, Jeff. There's nothing there."

"Maybe we can use a couple of clips in the interest of fairness. Let's take a look."

An imposing woman with a round, moonlike face appeared on the Moviola screen. Dr. Millicent Rogers was so well prepared for the interview that her responses had nothing at all to do with Jessica's questions. Her eulogies to McCampbell were unending. But when Jessica, her voice tinged with impatience, finally zoomed in on the subject of Styralon, she became defensive. "Our testing of the drug has not stopped, you know. Laboratory studies continue, and now that Styralon has been approved, we plan an extensive series of clinical tests to monitor its human application."

"Then it can be said," Jessica remarked, "that Styralon is still a highly experimental drug."

Dr. Rogers had her reply ready. "Certainly not. FDA approval is all that anyone needs to be certain of its absolute safety."

"Let's use that," Jessica told Jeff. "Her confidence in the government is really quite touching. And there was something else I forgot. She had nothing but praise for Dr. Bowen and his work. Let's see if we can find it."

"Why the switch?" Jeff asked. "Everybody else makes him the goat."

"I wondered about that. They obviously figured out that if all his Styralon reports were favorable, they couldn't make him sound completely crazy. And we should cut in a bit of her hymn of praise to McCampbell. That'll make Lyman's heart sing."

"And keep TML stock from plunging overnight. But damn it, Jess, we're adding stuff, not cutting."

"I know. It's hopeless."

At the end of the third week, they had a fine cut: fifty-eight minutes and thirteen seconds, allowing time for credits. But the film was far from finished. There was still the narration. From the rough script Jessica had prepared, she and Ann worked together to cut words and sentences, rearrange statistics, rephrase thoughts and images so the narration would fit into the spaces of silent film Jeff had left in the fine cut.

Her words would be recorded by Bill Tyson, one of Ben's masterful creations. Tyson's strong, resonant voice, craggy face, and avuncular but authoritative style had made him one of the most popular anchormen in the city and earned him the prestigious but low-paying job of chief reporter for the documentary unit's films. The word "reporter" was more than a bit misleading, an inside joke among the producers. Recording the narration script in a sound studio and two quick stand-uppers in front of Columbia-Presbyterian and the TML Building were all that would be necessary to establish Tyson as the correspondent of record. And when his measured words were added to the film, the implication would be that he was the one who had traveled around the world, putting the pieces of the Styralon puzzle together. It was Tyson, not Jessica, who coaxed evasions from Karl Engle, witnessed the quiet courage of the Harcents, listened to Daniel Bowen's dramatic story.

The recording session went well. Tyson's voice generally expressed just the mood and tone Jessica wanted for each section of the film. But then the soundtrack had to be fitted to the fine cut. And inevitably and maddeningly, the take in which the mood was right would be the one that ran too long. Or short. So she and Jeff had to move sentences around, cutting and splicing the soundtrack, just as they had cut and spliced the film.

"I think Bill's last take on London was the best," Jessica said, "even if he does sound a little bit like God. But it's eight seconds over. Can you tighten it?"

His teeth clamped on the stem of his unlit pipe, Jeff was examining a roll of film. "Look at this, Jess. I don't rewind this way. Tails out. Untaped."

"We were here until midnight," she said. "You were tired. You forgot."

"Never. I think someone was in here after we left, enjoying a private screening."

"No one could get through security at that hour."

"Unless they worked here."

"Lyman," Jessica said with a sigh. "Well, he had to see it sooner or later. The question is who saw it with him?"

Jeff rewound the soundtrack of Tyson's voice and the room was filled with the babble of words running backward through the machine. "It doesn't play, Jess," he said, turning down the speakers.

"Tyson's London take?"

"No. You. You're too serene about all the stuff going on around here. I know about the TML grant, and I know the pressure is on."

They had always shared every moment of making her films, from minor skirmishes with the crew to the stormy editorial clashes with Lyman, and Jessica felt disloyal. Her cool acceptance of what they both understood as excessive interference on this film seemed to shut Jeff out. "They want us to worry," she said. "Just as they wanted us to know they were here last night. There's nothing we can do about it."

"Okay," Jeff said, "as long as you see what's happening. But I have a feeling it isn't Wonderland this time, Alice. It's real trouble."

Later that afternoon, still cutting and splicing Tyson's soundtrack, they were interrupted by the ringing of the phone. "Yes, Counselor," Jeff said. "She's right here. A little frazzled but just as beautiful as ever."

"Sorry to bother you, Jess," Doug said, "but I wondered where you are on the film. Is it still scheduled for September?"

"The second Wednesday. Nine p.m."

"How does it look?"

"At this point, I'm hardly objective. But Jeff thinks Bowen is totally believable. And London is everything we hoped it would be."

There was a pause at the other end of the line, and realizing that London had been more than a location for her film, more than an interview with the Harcents, she regretted that she had been the one to bring it up. "What about the case?"

"Good news and bad. We got the temporary injunction but McCampbell is appealing, naturally. The court will hear the appeal very soon. If they find for McCampbell that would knock out the injunction and the drug could go on the market any day. But I've made a couple of new discoveries. Not a trace in the FDA files of the material Bowen gave them. I learned that from a lawyer there. But between your film and my case, the FDA is getting worried. And so is TML. Their lawyers and McCampbell's lawyers were palling around like old school chums at first. Now I'm happy to report there's a certain lack of harmony among them."

"Can you get away tomorrow?" Jessica asked.

"If it's important. Why?"

"We're mixing the film. It's the first chance to see what it really looks like and I think you should be there."

"I wouldn't miss it. Do I come to the station?"

"No, it's called PeriSound. 485 Lexington Avenue. Twentieth floor. At five."

"I'll be there."

For the rest of that day, late into the night, and most of the following day, Jessica and Jeff worked to lay the soundtrack against the film to get ready for the Mix. It was a long, laborious procedure, but Jessica's fatigue was tempered by excitement. She loved the Mix. It was only then that she knew she had a film. But with that exhilaration also came the first gnawing sense of loss. The Mix signaled the final phase of her work on the film. After that, it was over.

For once, Doug arrived before her. Waiting in the reception room of PeriSound Studios, he wondered which Jessica would walk through the door this time. Grudgingly, he had accepted the personal exile to which he had been consigned after their night in London, and was only mildly pleased that she had not excluded him from their professional relationship as well. But if that suited her, fine. He would look at the film critically, as a lawyer, to see if she had written or alleged anything that might jeopardize his case. Then he would do battle with her, not before.

He saw her enter the reception room, Jeff trailing behind, each of them loaded down with a large cardboard box. Jeff dropped his box on a table and waved. "I'll be right back. There's more in the taxi."

"We usually send all this stuff by messenger," Jessica said. "But this time I'm not taking any chances."

He followed her through the double doors that led to the studio, a long, antiseptic room with walls of dull gray vinyl and a floor of shiny gray tile. At one end of the room, there was a control board with enough buttons and dials to run a supersonic jet. At the other end, a large theater-sized screen was built flush into the wall. And suspended from the ceiling in every corner were large digital clocks, their red numbers set at 00:00:00. Filled with a numbing cold, the studio had the futuristic look of a space ship, an alien environment.

A corpulent man with a head of bushy hair framing a red-veined face was sitting in the chair in front of the control panel. Jessica introduced him to Doug as Ed Bridges, the Wizard of Sound. "So what are you selling today, beautiful?" he asked. "Whatever it is, I know I won't sleep for a week."

They had to wait while Jeff loaded the projectors. Finally he entered the studio and sat in a chair next to Jessica. "Okay, Jeff?" Bridges asked. And leaning forward he barked into a microphone, "This is a rehearsal. Defects of the Heart, Take One, Producer Lenhart. Let's do it."

Lights on the control panel blinked, the digital clocks clicked, and suddenly the large screen was filled with the face of Bill Tyson standing in front of Columbia-Presbyterian. But after he had said only a few sentences, Jessica grabbed Jeff's arm. "See, right there, how the background noise drops off."

"I missed that on the Moviola. That idiot hasn't got his mike on right."

"No problem," Bridges said. "I'll give you a little light traffic loop to fill it in."

Doug was disappointed. He had expected to see the film in its entirety, but every few seconds there was another interruption. And he recognized Tyson, but what the hell was he doing in Jessica's film? He understood finally what was going on. All extraneous sounds had to be erased from the film. And sounds that were muffled had to be enhanced. It took twenty minutes just to get rid of the drone of the airplane that had interrupted the interview with Madge Barwick. The film was rolled back and then forward again, each time with a sound accentuated or diminished until Bridges seemed satisfied with the level.

Jessica was just as critical. "Tyson sounds like he's auditioning for *Aida*," she remarked at one point. "Can't you take out some of the bass?" Then in a section of the Engle interview later in the film, he addressed her by name and she muttered, "Damn. I thought we cut that out."

"I couldn't. It was too tight," Jeff said. "Better to do it here."

"Not to worry," Bridges said complacently.

Doug had been puzzled by the face of Bill Tyson, then impressed by the skillful way he handled the material. Still it seemed deceptive, unfair, an act of electronic legerdemain, as if a lawyer had worked for months preparing a case and then hired an actor to argue it before a judge and jury. Tyson was asking Jessica's questions, uttering the words of her script, but she herself was nowhere to be found. During several of the interviews, Doug had heard her ask not to be called by name. Now he knew why, and as he watched her erase even the tiniest vestige of her own personality from the soundtrack, he was gaining respect for her professional competence, but new contempt for the medium in which she worked. It was one thing for a business to ask you to whore, to bury your principles in a hundred little pragmatic acts. But to give up your identity? He had been right about television, right about her as a woman. She was comfortable only behind a camera, at home only in this chilly, computer-controlled environment where clocks ticked off every microsecond. She won awards in a business that made its profits by selling time.

He didn't want to see this. Stop. Start. Stop. Start. Tinkering with sound, raising and lowering voices as if they were something mechanical, inhuman. Timmy Harcent was the worst. The film showed him climbing laboriously up the ladder of his slide, waving when he reached the top, and then pushing himself off with a shriek of laughter.

"Jesus," Bridges said. "The needle went right into space. I've got to fix that."

He reversed the film and Timmy slid back up the slide, then down and up again, like some comic effect in a home movie, while Bridges adjusted the sound of his joyous laughter. Doug turned his face away from the screen.

After three hours it was finally over, the clocks fixed at 56:00:00. "You want some music under the credits?" Bridges asked.

"No, we'll run them silent," Jeff answered. "The light loop I put behind them is fine."

Bridges pressed a switch and red, yellow, and green lights blinked as the computers whirred, registering the levels of sound he had recorded during the rehearsal. "Okay, that's it. I'll get some coffee. Then we'll look at it and see if it's a buy."

He turned on the overhead lights before he left the studio, and it was then that Doug saw how drained Jessica looked. The angles of her face were sharp, her body slumped in a chair, registering fatigue.

"That was a hell of a way to see it for the first time, Counselor," Jeff said. "You'll like it better straight through."

Jessica didn't say a word.

Bridges returned, passed out containers of coffee, and then the room was dark again except for the winking of the tiny lights on the control panel. The red numbers of the digital clocks worked their way back to zero.

Doug wondered how many times Jessica had seen every frame, listened to every word of the film. Could she still care about it after such deadening repetition? But he saw her straighten in her chair, once again alert; the expression on her face, illuminated only by the rainbow-colored lights, was one of anticipation that was almost sensual. She knew what was about to happen.

He didn't. And from the opening scene in Dr. Rudnick's laboratory to the frozen close-up of Timmy Harcent at the end of the film, it was as if he had never heard of Styralon. It was all there: the ducks paddling in the pond in front of McCampbell's bucolic headquarters, the glass-fronted facade of TML's city fortress, the factory-like building that housed Chanterelle, the Harcents' tiny garden. And the faces: Dr. Rudnick's benign expression as he held a deformed mouse in the palm of his hand, Karl Engle gnawing his lips and stroking his beard, Madge Barwick and her fluttery loss of memory, Timmy nestled between his parents on their living room sofa, Daniel Bowen's haunted eyes. The facts and figures were there, too, the statistics from England, the complexities of the drug approval process, woven into a script that was both subtle and spare. Fraud, perjury, criminal conspiracy were never mentioned and barely implied. The protagonists spoke for themselves and the clash of realities was underscored in the jarring juxtaposition of their words. Doug forgot to take notes, completely caught up in the story. It wasn't an abstraction—money and power. It was about people. He was moved, outraged, and finally overwhelmed by the humanity, the feeling, of the film. Even if her voice wasn't on the soundtrack, or her face on a single frame, that feeling could only be Jessica's.

Then it was over and the credits began to roll in silence. The names went by: Jessica Lenhart, Ann Berris, Jeff Russell. And the acknowledgments: "The producers would like to express their appreciation to the Public Interest Law Cooperative and Mr. Douglas Weber for their assistance in the preparation of this broadcast." The copyright slide appeared and the clocks stopped at 58:13:00, not a second more, not a second less.

Bridges, obviously moved, was the first to speak. "Jesus, I don't know how you two do it. That kid . . . "

"Doug, is it okay?" Jessica's voice was strangely thin.

"Okay? It's fantastic."

"Will anything cause you a problem in court?"

"I think it's McCampbell's problem now. You've both done a hell of a job."

"Thanks," Jeff said. "How about joining us for a celebration? Drinks at Johnny's. It's a tradition after the Mix."

Doug watched fascinated as they began packing up the film. Jessica was exultant, her face radiant as she laughed and joked with Jeff, and he felt like a voyeur observing the afterplay of two lovers coming down from an intensely shared moment. Carrying one of the boxes, he followed them into the reception room.

"Are you Mr. Weber?" the woman behind the desk asked. "I've got a message for you."

He looked at the slip, then picked up the phone and dialed a number.

"Come on," Jessica called. "Jeff's getting a taxi."

"Go on without me," he said, putting down the phone.

"Doug, what is it? What's happened?"

"That was Wendy. Mel's had a heart attack."

"Oh, no."

"I have to go to the hospital."

"I'll come with you."

"You don't have to."

"Of course I do."

There was a small waiting room adjacent to the Special Cardiac Care Unit of Lenox Hill. Wanda was pacing, her eyes behind the horn-rimmed glasses bruised by the black and blue smudges of her makeup. "I wish I smoked," she said. "It would give me something to do."

"How is he?" Doug looked at her anxiously.

"We don't know yet."

"What happened?" Jessica asked.

Wanda's laugh was mirthless. "He collapsed at the goddamn gym. Isn't that a kick in the ass? I'm the one who made him go there. But maybe it was lucky in a way. They knew what it was and what to do. I was dressing to meet him for dinner when the hospital called. And would you like to hear my mature reaction? I couldn't let Mel see me until I did my hair, finished my makeup. Look at me. I'm a mess."

She stopped pacing and sat down in a hard black plastic chair. "Well, you can't say we didn't see it coming. The grayness in his face, his rotten moods. He was working too hard. Damn it, you *all* work too hard. And you want to hear another mature reaction? I used to think I could make it on my own. But I can't. Not now, not without Mel. I love him. I can't lose him."

"Can we see him?" Jessica asked.

"Yes, one at a time. He's conscious, but they don't want him to talk."

"You go first, Jess," Doug said.

"Where the hell were you?" Wanda asked angrily after Jessica left the waiting room. "Wendy couldn't find you anywhere."

"Watching Jessica's film. It's finished. She's done a great job."

"Well, that's something. And the other part of Mel's little plan? I know. Not so great. I'm sorry."

"But not surprised."

Wanda shrugged. "How can two smart guys be so dumb?"

"What are you talking about?"

"Thursdays. Jessica's life is measured out in Thursdays."

"What's so special about Thursdays?"

Too tired to lie, as mad at everyone as she was at herself, Wanda said flatly, "She makes love."

"How do you know? Did she tell you?"

"She didn't have to. After someone turns down enough Thursday night invitations, comes to parties alone and leaves alone, you finally catch on. At least, I did. And you're not the first man Mel has trotted out for her inspection. They didn't get very far either."

"Who is he?"

"Do you care?"

"Yes, I guess I do."

"Well, he's married. That should be obvious. You look surprised. What did you think she was, a nun?"

"I thought a lot of things. Still it's comforting to know the lady has room for love in her life."

"Love," Wanda said bitterly. "What do either one of you know about love? You with your Bambis, and Jessica with some phantom Thursday night lover who cheats on his wife. I've been a Bambi. I've been a Jessica. It's not so different. And believe me, they both stink."

Rummaging in her purse, Wanda found her compact and peering into the tiny mirror began to repair her face. "Oh hell, what's the use?" she said, snapping the compact shut. "It's none of my business what you do with your lives. Save the world from nine to five and then crawl into bed at night with a stranger you can get rid of in the morning. Who knows why? Maybe you're selfish. Maybe you're scared. Either way you end up alone. Take my advice . . . " Wanda cut her words short when she saw Jessica standing in the doorway of the waiting room.

"They only let me stay for a minute," Jessica said. "But I caught Mel winking at the nurse."

"That son of a bitch," Wanda muttered. "I'll kill him."

Doug left them together and walked through the deserted

corridor to the nurse's station. "Mr. Shane," he told the woman at the desk. She directed him to Mel's room where a nurse, pressing a finger to her lips, warned him to be quiet.

Mel was flat on his back under a plastic oxygen tent, his heartbeat recorded in green blips on a television monitor. And for an instant, Doug saw another figure lying on a hospital bed. But Mel was not the skeleton of a man his father had been. His face was ruddy, his big body heaved rhythmically with the effort of his breathing. Intrusive, domineering, critical, a pain in the ass—but alive. And Doug's thoughts echoed Wanda's words: "I can't lose him."

The nurse pointed to her watch and as Doug turned to leave, Mel stirred. His eyes were open and his smile was only a pale simulation of the seven-letter variety. But there was triumph in it. He raised his hand from the sheet and made a fist, thrusting his thumb upward. Doug returned his salute.

"He's going to make it," he said, after rejoining Wanda and Jessica in the waiting room.

"Yes," Wanda agreed. "The doctor said he was lucky. It was a warning."

"Thank God," Jessica sighed.

"Who? What the hell does God have to do with it? With anything? There's a chapel right next door. Did you see it? How's that for covering your bets?"

What happens now?" Doug asked.

"Another day or so here," Wanda replied. "And then they begin tests to find out if there's any permanent damage. He'll probably come home in a week. But I'm taking him out to the beach house. Maybe if I can get him away from this damned city, he'll slow down."

"Is there anything I can do?" Doug said.

"Yes. Lie. Tell him nobody wants him, nobody needs him. Tell him the world won't go spinning off into space if he's not around for a few weeks. Tell him I'd look lousy in black."

"Is there anything we can do for you?" Jessica asked. She spoke to Wanda but her mind was filled with a montage of faces. Women in love. Beryl, torn with grief, as if she had lost not only her husband but a vital part of herself. Laurel Harcent refusing to admit that death was preferable to imperfection. Bertha Bowen fighting to protect her husband from a form of self-destruction as insidious as the illness that had claimed their son. And Wanda ready to battle anyone, even Mel, to save his life. Where would she be, Jessica wondered, if something happened to Ben? Sneaking through empty hospital corridors, a shadowy night visitor, stealing into his room only after Sara and the children had gone. And when they were old, would she still be living in the margins of his life, on the outside, her nose pressed against the glass, looking in?

"For me?" Wanda said. "There's nothing you can do for me. I thought I was home free, damn it. Hard-edged New York dame, who's seen more ceilings than Michelangelo, meets brilliant but cantankerous lawyer. Lawyer ignores wear and tear on dame and suddenly, this slightly used, slightly menopausal lady finds love. It's no secret. I got where I am on my back. But with all the others, even the ones I married, I closed my eyes. With Mel, my eyes were wide open, always. Even at the start, he *mattered*. Simple, isn't it? A match made in heaven, right? Wrong. *We* made it, and we're making it work because we know this isn't an audition, an out-of-town preview. This is it, opening night. Sure, maybe the leading man has a bum heart; maybe the leading lady is no ingenue. But who gives a damn what the critics say? We signed a run-of-the-play contract, and this show is going to last."

Wanda refused to cry. She stuck her glasses on top of her

head and covered her eyes with her hand. "Christ, talk about overacting," she said. "Yes, there is something you can do. Keep the office away from him, will you, Doug? And Jessica, I'll tell him about your film. Doug says it's wonderful. That'll cheer him up. He loves you, you know. Both of you. Come see us at the beach house. I'm going to need help to keep him quiet. Now get the hell out of here. Mel's sons and their wives are on their way and I don't want you watching when I play that scene. They think I'm driving their poor dear father to a premature death. And I'm going to tell them, just as sweetly as I know how, that Mel Shane will be around to dance a jig on their miserable graves."

The day had been very long. But wrenched from the exhilaration of the Mix to the sadness of Mel's illness, they decided to have their celebration anyway. Doug suggested his apartment, which was only a few blocks from the hospital, and implicit in both his invitation and Jessica's acceptance was their wish to regain some kind of equilibrium, to balance their emotional pitches, to blend and neutralize words spoken and words left unspoken between them.

There were no sexual overtones in his invitation. She felt no sexual threat. Rather, the feeling was one of impending loss. Jessica realized that with the completion of the film, there would be little reason to see Doug again. He shared that realization, but in Mel's battle against mortality, he sensed a deeper deprivation. So neither of them wanted the day to end. Or if it must, it deserved some notice, a rite to mark its passage.

"I've got a bottle of white wine in the refrigerator," he said. "I knew I was saving it for something."

Jessica resisted the temptation to inspect his apartment as carefully as he had inspected hers. But from the moment he opened the door, she was surprised. It was too large for one

person. She had never imagined that he might be lonely.

She was leaning against the railing of the terrace when he returned with the wine. Tall, angular buildings obscured the view of the river. But the dull yellow glow of Long Island was framed by the swags of light on the Queensboro Bridge. "I'd sell my soul for a view like this," she said.

"That's exactly what I did. But Mel took the case to court and we got it back." He poured the wine and raising their glasses they said in unison, "To Mel."

"I grew up over there," Doug said, "at the other end of the bridge. Went to high school, worked in a warehouse nights while I was going to college. I couldn't wait to get out, and I'm not sure why I like looking at it now, even from a distance."

"Did you always want to be a lawyer?"

"I wanted to be someone. But I didn't know what I wanted to do."

"I was the other way around. I knew what I wanted to do before I knew who I wanted to be."

"Where did you grow up?"

"A placid Chicago suburb. Trees, grass, hopscotch on the sidewalk, my tricycle parked in the driveway. Safe, protected by an abundance of love."

"That's another difference between us. Why do I have the feeling I'll never get to know you?"

"I thought you'd be happy to be rid of me."

"I thought so, too." Doug refilled their glasses. "Then that's it. Your work on the film is over."

"Pretty much. The rest is technical. Jeff sends the print you saw today to a man with bad eyesight, who matches it to the negative and plays with the color and light until we get a perfect answer print."

"And then?"

"Then we begin showing it. The lawyers first. They've

seen most of it already and Jeff went crazy splicing in all the 'allegeds.' But they'll ask to see it again. And then my boss has to give it a final look."

"Your boss?"

"Ben Nevins."

"Will he object to anything?"

"Ben? No. He's seen most of it, too. And if it weren't for Ben, there wouldn't be a documentary unit at the station. He fought for that, and for every film I've ever made."

"With whom?"

"The lawyers, the station brass, Lyman Ellis."

"I've heard of him."

"Lyman would be pleased," Jessica said. "He usually doesn't concern himself with such lowly matters as a documentary. But this time there's the TML connection, and Jeff and I suspect he's already helped himself to a private screening."

"Could he stop the film?"

"Not now. It's too late. And if he tried, we might leak a little item to the press. So there are a few things left to do: work on the ads if the station decides to spend some money on advertising, which will never happen on this film; act the charming but very anxious hostess at press screenings and pray for good reviews. Then I wait and watch it on television like everyone else."

"And with some luck, and your film, I may have an injunction by then," Doug said. "Is it possible we finally got our timing right?"

He started to refill her glass, but she shook her head. "I have to go."

"When will I see you again?"

"You heard what Wanda said. We've both got another battle on our hands with Mel."

In the silence of the night, they could hear music drifting

from the open windows of another apartment; the buzz of traffic from the street below sounded like wind rustling through the trees.

"Then there's something else we have to talk about," Doug said. "London."

"What's there to say?" Jessica responded immediately. "What happened happened. It was so intense, Doug. London, filming Timmy Harcent. You knew how I felt."

"Of course I did. I was there, too, remember? But you never asked how I felt. You just used me to ward off your dark thoughts about yourself and your profession. I was a drug, a painkiller. Don't I at least deserve an acknowledgement for that? 'The producer would like to thank Douglas Weber for being an accomplice in an act of personal redemption.' But Jessica Lenhart reclaims her soul, retrieves her humanity, and then walks away untouched. Just as she always does."

His words were harsh, and because of the wine, or her fatigue, or perhaps because she recognized the truth of his accusation, her words were sharp, too. "No. You're wrong. I didn't ask you to stay. I didn't ask you to make love to me. And what was I to you that night?"

"You were a woman I had never met before, a woman I haven't seen since. I thought we had both found something new, Jess. But I guess I was wrong. I wasn't any different from the people you film. You coax, woo, seduce, flash your credit card, and after you get what you want, you disappear."

"Just because you finally saw me as more than a woman with a camera or a plaque, that's not a seduction. I was sad and empty that night, Doug. You took advantage of that."

"Then that's why you ran out of the room, why you've treated me like a leper ever since. Didn't you see me as anyone different? Wasn't there something, anything, about that night you want to remember?"

It was a question she would not answer. "Doug, please. I don't want to argue with you, not today, not after all that's happened. If I've hurt you, or made you angry, I'm sorry."

"You're damn right I'm angry, but at least I think I'm beginning to understand. I saw you this afternoon, deliberately removing every trace of yourself from your own film. Your name, your voice. It's part of your business."

"That's not fair," Jessica said. "My business is not my life."

"It shouldn't be. And whether you know it or not, you're still in that film, every minute of it. Not the Jessica you think you have to be, but the woman I met in London. I guess I'm sorry to see her disappear again."

Jessica smiled. "I suppose that's a compliment."

"And it's probably my fault, not yours."

"Won't you even plea bargain?" Jessica asked. "What kind of lawyer are you? I plead guilty, too."

"And our sentence?"

"After a brief period of probation, may I suggest we try friendship?"

She offered him her hand and he took it, both of them amused by the slight absurdity of the gesture.

"I'll give a party here the night your film airs," Doug said. "Mel and Wanda, Jeff. Some of your friends, some of mine."

"I'd like that. And can I come to court?"

"Of course. You might enjoy it. I put on quite a show."

"We both put on quite a show."

"But in case you haven't guessed, Jess, I intend to win this one."

EIGHTEEN

Ben drove into his parking space, locked the car, and strode quickly toward the station. He bought a paper as the train hissed to a stop alongside the platform, and pulling himself up the steps, he found a seat. Outside the air was crisp with the first hint of autumn; inside it was foul with the odor of tobacco smoke. The floor was dirty, the upholstery torn and dusty, the windows opaque. The man next to him was asleep, his chin on his chest, snoring.

Unfolding the paper, Ben glanced at the headlines, but his mind was still crackling with the noises of the night before, like static on the radio that persists after an electrical storm has passed. Through dinner and later in the living room, he and Sara had talked, read, listened to music as they always did. There was no sign that anything was different. Even in their bedroom, the scene was familiar; he was already in bed while Sara, in her nightgown, sat at the dressing table, brushing her hair. Then, speaking to the mirror, she said, "Ben, I've decided to take some classes in New York this fall. I want to get my degree and then look for a job. Is that all right with you?"

"Of course it's all right," he said. But he wondered if it meant she would again begin the talk about cashing in their quiet suburban chip to play for higher stakes: an apartment in the city. For he knew the years they had spent in New York, while the children were young and he was working as a journalist, were equated in her mind with the life, the energy, their marriage now seemed to lack.

"I'd have to commute at least three days a week," Sara said.

"What price education." There was humor in his voice, along with an inner sense of relief.

Sara moved to the edge of the bed and leaned over to kiss him. Her lips were soft, her body accepting. He held her for a moment and then pulled away.

Displeased with himself, he found an excuse in remembering that while their sexual encounters had diminished quite naturally with time, only in recent years, on Wednesdays, was he alone responsible. Then, like an athlete the night before a championship game, he saved himself, hoarded his passion, for Jessica. He wished he could explain —another night, yes. Still he could not pretend he hadn't been aroused by Sara's kiss.

She returned to the dressing table, her hands clasped in

her lap. "Do you want a divorce?" she asked, her words uttered with a surprising lack of emotion. "Because if you do, it's all right. I'll be all right."

"Sara, I'm tired. That's all."

"No, that's not all. Is there someone else?"

"You bet there is. Thirty-five people in the office are clamoring for my attention every day. Producers complaining about budgets, editors griping about antique equipment, and if Lyman had his way, my department would be producing a series on heroes of American capitalism."

"Then it's me," Sara said sadly. "It's us. We're in trouble, Ben, and you won't tell me what it is or why."

Humor, sarcasm, what else could he use to deflect the complexities that her words implied? For four years he had imagined this conversation, only he thought that some day Sara would find out about Jessica and her words would be shrill, accusatory, bitter. But she knew nothing. She blamed herself, offering him an escape clause in a contract he had thought inviolate. Why shouldn't he invoke it? No one would be hurt, and in his life with Jessica, there would be weeks, months, years of Thursdays. He had often imagined that, too. Jessica was adventure, a sea voyage to an unexplored island. But Sara was home, familiar, a safe harbor. A man should have both, needed both. And with that thought, Ben realized the true gravity of Sara's offer. Without even knowing there was an alternative, she was forcing him to choose.

He got out of bed and stood behind her at the dressing table. Their eyes met in the mirror as he stroked the back of her neck. "I love you, Sara," he said. "You know that."

"I love you, too. That's not the issue. I'm speaking of our life. If we can't be together, then I'd rather be alone."

"You don't mean that," he said, kissing the top of her head. She turned, their lips met, and he knew he was merely postponing the moment when they would have to reconstruct what they once had been, or abandon what was left. But in bed, forgetting his vow of Wednesday night chastity, he had made love to his wife.

The man in the seat next to him snored himself awake and mumbled an apology. Ben opened his paper, beginning as he always did with the television news, his thoughts still of Sara, Jessica, his job. Every day pieces of himself were being eaten away—by Lyman's encroachments, by Sara's gentle demands, by age and time. Only Jessica saw him as he wanted to be seen. Never once had she asked him for more than he was able to give.

His eye caught a small headline at the bottom of the page: "New Music Series for WPTN." More opera, he thought sourly as he scanned the article. "Today Lyman Ellis announced a grant of two million dollars to his station earmarked for a series of concerts of the music of Vivaldi, which will be broadcast live from the auditorium of the Whitney Museum." He had to hand it to Lyman. Twenty million dollars from TML, two million dollars for Vivaldi. The money was rolling in. "Premiering Wednesday, September 7, the series will continue for twenty-six weeks." That's a big dose of Vivaldi. "To accommodate this unexpected but very welcome addition to our fall schedule, Mr. Ellis said, we will postpone the premier of our distinguished public affairs series, 'WPTN Reports,' until the beginning of next year."

"Postpone . . . next year." Ben's eyes focused on the words and he read the article again. "That bastard," he said out loud.

He folded the paper into his attaché case and leaned back against the musty seat, his head reverberating with the clacking of the train. Then, unable to breathe, he got up, walked the length of the aisle, and standing on the bridge between the cars, let the cool air rush against his face. It was very clear and very clever. Lyman had dumped not only Jessica's film but the entire documentary series. What would he tell his producers? And what in Christ's name could he say to Jessica?

She thought it was a perfect morning, a day so clear that even the drabbest buildings shone in the sharp sunlight. Riding the bus uptown, Jessica stared out of the window at the people on the streets and the fresh, near chaotic energy of the morning rush hour. But she, for a change, wasn't in a hurry to do anything. It would be an easy day, with time to read the paper, chat with Ann while they waited for an answer print from the lab, a long lunch and perhaps an hour or so browsing through the stores to look for something to wear this fall. She didn't feel, as she often did after the Mix, the need to begin searching for another story. Not yet. Today was for herself, and her mood was one of exhilaration. The film was finished and almost ready for screenings. She and Doug had finally negotiated a friendly truce and she could erase the memory of their night in London. Mel's heart was just as tough as he was.

And Ben. It was Thursday, and she anticipated an evening with him not the way they had begun, nor the way they had become these past few weeks when everything seemed so intense and slightly distorted. She would leave work early, shop and cook dinner for him in her apartment. It didn't have to be the Ritz; there was no need for roses.

She had a smile for the security guard, a smile for the people in the elevator. She was smiling when she walked into her office. Jeff was there, his unlit pipe clenched between his teeth, talking to Ann. They were not smiling.

"What's the matter with you two?" Jessica asked. "You must have had quite a celebration last night. Cheer up. The film is mixed, it's a gorgeous day, and you look like you've lost a friend."

"A film," Ann said. "We've lost a film. Haven't you seen the paper?"

"What are you talking about?"

"It's right here in black and white," Jeff said, shoving the newspaper at her. "Your film is out. The whole series is out."

Searching the page, Jessica found the article and read it slowly with bewilderment, then disbelief, which gave way to a shattering sense of betrayal. "Why didn't Ben tell me?"

"There's a rumor he didn't find out himself until this morning," Ann said.

"I've got to talk to him," Jessica said, throwing the paper on her desk and starting for the door.

"Save it, Jess. There's a staff meeting at ten. And at the moment, Ben is, as they say, 'in seclusion.'"

He took off his jacket, loosened his tie, rolled up his shirt-sleeves. This was going to be tricky. His producers, he knew, would be both angry and frightened, for Lyman's latest fiat meant more than a simple delay in the schedule. It threatened their jobs. Ben could not defend Lyman's decision without sounding like a corporate lackey. But if he shared their anger, poured out his own sense of indignation and betrayal, he would seem equally impotent in their eyes. He had to separate himself from Lyman, yet offer them some reason to continue to trust his own authority.

The balance was crucial. And in time he would find it. While Lyman traded in the currency of power, appeals to conscience and guilt were still negotiable commodities. And Ben could use them to bargain for a slice of the TML grant for his unit. But Lyman, his sense of timing as exquisite as always, was out of town, in Washington, or so Ben had been told, and wouldn't return until tomorrow. That unpleasant piece of business would have to wait. His producers had to be reassured, placated today. All except Jessica. They could talk tonight.

Voices that had been raised in heated discussion suddenly lowered as they filed into his office like visitors entering the home of the bereaved. Irv Seiden wore an expression of injury and sad confusion. Howard Tarr's lips were compressed with rage. Larry Higby, who had recently accepted a job with a commercial station, assumed the air of a distant relation, a mildly interested mourner. Uncharacteristically, Jessica was the last to arrive. She ignored the stares of the others as she took her usual seat on the couch at the far end of the room. She could not look at Ben.

"This won't take long," he began. "I'm certain that being the scrupulous journalists you are, you've read the morning paper. So did I, but with amazement, not surprise. I don't have to remind any of you that this kind of crap comes with the territory."

"A little crap I can handle," Tarr said bitterly. "But this time we're buried in it, and I want to know why."

"I think we all know why, Howard," Ben replied. "The money that comes to this station has always had strings attached. Even for Vivaldi."

No one laughed and Ben spoke quickly to fill the awkward silence. "I haven't seen Lyman yet, but I assure you he has no intention of killing this unit."

"No, he'll just let it linger, crippled and comatose," Higby muttered.

"But if Jessica's film was the problem," Seiden asked, his voice a whine, "why didn't Lyman just cancel that?"

"For the same reason," Ben said, "that he couldn't cancel one of your ghetto films last summer because he thought it might sow the seeds of 'urban discontent.' I can't justify what he did, Irv, but that was the only way he could do it."

"Then why the hell didn't *you* cancel it?" Tarr demanded. "And please spare us a lot of sanctimonious bullshit about freedom of the press. It was stupid to let Jessica make a film about TML. You were begging for trouble. I've got a wife and a kid and a mortgage and you can talk forever about the tragic demise of documentaries. What about the tragic demise of my job?"

Ben felt the stinging rebuke of Tarr's words even as he understood the depth of his sycophancy. "Jessica was working on this story long before there was even a hint of the TML grant. To ask her to stop when the grant was announced would be irresponsible. A blatant sellout."

"So you sold out the entire unit," Tarr cried indignantly. "Where's your responsibility to the rest of us? Shouldn't that transcend your interest in one particular film—or one particular producer?"

"Howard," Higby growled, "I never realized what a horse's ass you really are."

"You god-damned coward! You're leaving and you have the nerve . . ."

"Okay," Ben said, raising his hands like a schoolteacher trying to quiet a roomful of unruly students. "That's enough. I've defended your films, too, Howard. And if Jessica can't be allowed to make the kind of films she wants to make, none of us can."

"Sure, but why is it always *her* films that cause the trouble? What's she got around here, some kind of special license?"

Ben felt a flush rising in his face, aware that Tarr was accusing him of something more than mere favoritism. "I think you're missing the point, Howard," he said. "I understand your feelings, but I can't agree that Jessica, or anyone else in this unit, has done something wrong."

Sitting on the couch, chin cupped in her hand, Jessica was again the observer, outside the scene, listening to the other producers speak of her as if she weren't there. But now she had to defend herself from Tarr's accusations and innuendos. "Your argument is with Lyman, not with me, Howard. I had no way of knowing what he would do. And this film is important . . . "

"Oh Christ, come off it!" Tarr shouted. "This isn't a calling. It's a job. Why don't you join the rest of us down here on earth? That's what really kills me, your holier-than-thou attitude, the liberal do-goodism that's part of every frame of film you've ever made."

"Oh shut up," Seiden said in an unusual burst of assertion. "I remember that attitude. I had it when I was Jessica's age."

"You still do." Higby sighed.

"No one has ever complained about your politics," Jessica said, countering Tarr's rancor with her own quiet rage. "Construction workers spouting racist epithets to protect their jobs. High school principals defending book burning. Wide-angle tributes to narrow little minds. I can't challenge the fact that your films are a faithful EKG of the heart of some Americans, Howard. Why won't you allow me the same grace? The country has many hearts."

"All right," Ben said, "let's leave politics *and* personalities out of this. If I didn't believe all of your films were important, I wouldn't be here and neither would you. Jessica just happens to be the one who pushed Lyman to the wall and we've got to figure out some way to live with it."

"No, Ben, I disagree," Jessica said, looking at him directly for the first time. "I'm not sure I *can* live with it. You can worry about the First Amendment, the future of the unit, the lack of guts at this station, and I'm worried, too. But I'm also worried about the women who might take that drug if it isn't stopped. If that's too holy for you, Howard, I apologize. But I won't apologize for the film or my reasons for making it."

"Bravo," Higby said.

"I think Jessica is right," Ben said. "You're all talking as if the unit is dead. It isn't. We've got four films in the can with the promise of a new series the first of the year. I'm going to hold Lyman to that promise. And I want all of you back in here next week with ideas for your new films."

Seiden's expression was one of non-comprehension. "Are you saying all our films will air, including Jessica's?"

"I'm saying that as far as I know, Vivaldi didn't write any requiems. And I'm also saying this meeting is over."

It felt like rape. Her film was dead and it felt like rape. She was stunned, outraged, but why was she surprised? Jeff had warned her, Kate and Paul, and she had ignored them all, as if she were untouchable, inviolate. What would she tell Bertha and Daniel Bowen, Jack and Laurel Harcent, everyone who had come forward, exposing their pain because of the promises she had made? And what of the promises she had made to Doug? If television had never demanded that she sell her body, she had wooed, lured, seduced them all. And how could it be rape when she herself had been so compliant, her innocence a wink, her passion for her work just another come-on? She was like the woman who walks the streets, breasts and thighs exposed, beckoning customers, then crazily calling foul.

"So what do we do now?" Ann said glumly.

They sat behind the closed door of their office, survivors of a catastrophe, too dazed to think or move.

"I don't know," Jessica said.

"We have to write some letters," Ann reminded her. "The Bowens, the Harcents, Madge Barwick. And you've got to call Doug."

"I dread it."

She could not reach him. He was in court, Wendy said, arguing a case for Mel, but she would give him a message as soon as he called in.

Jessica remembered how she had planned to spend the day: a long lunch, shopping. But in spite of her gloom, she couldn't leave the office now. She and Ann ordered coffee and sandwiches, and going down the list of everyone who appeared in the film, they wrote to notify them that it had been postponed. Each letter exacted its own emotional price. Karl Engle would be relieved, Jessica knew; Madge Barwick, disappointed. But the Harcents might not mind. They at least would have recourse in the courts. And Daniel Bowen? With his last hope snatched away, his reaction could only be one of despair.

Finally Doug called. "All hell's breaking loose, Jess. With Mel out of action, I've got more work than I can handle and McCampbell knows it. This case could go on for months. Thank God for your film. It's the one thing that can break this legal log jam. I've spoken to Mel, and he agrees. And Wanda says if he behaves himself, they'll both be at our party."

"There isn't going to be a party."

"Why not?"

"There isn't going to be a film."

"I don't understand. What's wrong?"

"It's in the morning paper. Lyman Ellis has canceled the entire series."

"How can he do that? Damn it, Jess. I knew something like this was going to happen."

"I'm sorry, Doug. It took us all by surprise."

"To hell with sorry. We can get that bastard. I'm a lawyer, remember? We'll sue him for infringement of your First Amendment rights, conflict of interest, breach of contract. You name it, you've got it."

Jessica couldn't help laughing. "You sound more like Mel every day."

"And you sound like you're going to accept this without a fight."

"No, I've got to fight. But I need time to figure out which way to go."

"What about your boss? You said he liked the film."

"Doug, please. I'll do everything I can. But for once, I've run out of promises."

"Okay, that's what I wanted to hear. I didn't mean to bark, but I guess I was counting on your film more than I realized. Let me know if there's anything I can do to help."

"You can call Mel," Jessica said. "But go easy. I don't want him to have another attack. And thanks."

"For what?"

"Your views on television are well known. Thanks for not saying, 'I told you so.' "

Part of her wish for their evening was answered as the Thursday night rituals went unobserved. She met Ben in the lobby of her apartment building and they walked through crowded Village streets toward Ernesto's. The night air was filled with a hodgepodge of ethnic aromas, and tourists gawked at other tourists imagining them to be natives of this strange, unconventional place.

"Look at them," Jessica said. "After sniffing an hour of Bohemian air, they'll all return home, with an ounce of grass in their pockets, convinced of the rightness of their own lives." The anger that had been building all afternoon was now so great that it was aimed at anything that smacked of hypocrisy dressed up as moral superiority, anyone who reminded her of Lyman Ellis.

"Come on, Jess. That's not like you. We've always loved it down here. You'll feel better after we've had something to eat."

"I'm not hungry. Let's go back. We've got to talk."

Moving swiftly and in silence along one of the quiet side streets that led back to her apartment, they passed two young men with locked arms who noticed the grim distance between them. "Heterosexual love on the rocks," their knowing grins seemed to say.

Other rituals were ignored. There were no flowers; they did not pause for their standard embrace in the hallway of her apartment. Instead, Ben dropped his attaché case on the hall table and went into the living room. "I read it in the paper this morning, Jess, just like you."

"But you must have known. I asked you last week if there was something going on with Lyman."

"And I told you then, there's *always* something going on with Lyman. But I didn't know he'd go this far. How do you think I feel right now?"

"And how do you think *I* feel?" Jessica demanded. "Howard was right. My film has jeopardized the future of the whole unit. You should have told me, you should have warned me, Ben. You've seen the film. You said it's the best thing I've ever done. We could have shown it to Lyman, gotten to him somehow. Or gotten around him. Now it's too late. The film is dead."

"It isn't dead. Your film will air, I promise you."

"Where? When? After Doug has won his case, after everything explodes and the drug has already been taken off the market? By then it'll be yesterday's headlines. A footnote. A relic."

Ben sat on the couch and tried to draw her down beside him. "Darling, listen to me . . . "

She pulled away. "I don't feel like listening and I don't feel like darling. I feel indulged, patronized."

"It's the nature of love to protect."

"It's *not* the nature of love to exclude."

"You don't understand, Jess. That's part of my job, not just with you but with everyone else in the unit. I'm the heat shield between you and Lyman. If I came to you every time he had a gripe, wanted a script change or had some self-serving idea of his own, nothing would get done in the unit. Sure, I knew he objected to your film. I've known it for weeks. And I knew why. But what was the point of telling you?"

"Then, you treated me like a child. And I hate that, just as I hate what Lyman is doing to you. Using you. Acting like the station is his own private fiefdom and then selling out to the lordly TML. And you might be interested to know that while you were so busy protecting me, the long arm of TML stole my file from Kate Marchand's office."

"Kate Marchand? Paul's wife? She's a psychiatrist. Why the hell are you going to a psychiatrist?"

"I didn't know how to handle my mother after my father died. Kate helped me and then we became friends. That was two years ago, Ben, but somehow TML found out about it and sent someone to spy on Kate."

"Do Paul and Kate know about us?"

"Of course. I told Kate, and after my files were stolen, she had to tell Paul. Why do you look so shocked? Everybody knows. What do you think Howard meant this morning about my special license? Lyman knows, too. If the Vivaldi grant hadn't come through, he would have used that to stop the film."

Running his fingers through the sparseness of his hair, Ben slumped back on the couch. "Jesus, Jess. I had no idea."

She sat down beside him. "Oh, Ben, I don't mean to take all this out on you. But don't you see, I'm not a child."

"But you are an idealist and that's what I love about you. That's what I was trying to protect."

"Cynicism is the flip side of idealism. You once told me that's what you needed in your department."

"But not in my life." He moved toward her on the couch, reached out to hold her. "Let's not argue, Jess. This is our night. When Lyman gets back tomorrow, I'll talk to him. We can work something out, I know. But tonight let's forget about him." His lips brushed her ear and he whispered, "I can make you forget."

The tenderness in his eyes, the gentleness of his hands disarmed her for a moment. Once more, she realized, he was treating her like a child. Yet his words, his touch were those of a man arousing a woman who was allowed to emerge only in his arms. And even those moments were protected by rituals, gilded with romance. The realities of who they were, his marriage, her job, were never allowed to intrude. She thought of her father and the tiny perfect jewel he had presented to her mother on every anniversary. Ben had given her the gem of his protection, and only now was she forced to think of the cost. How many compromises had he made with Lyman? How had he conspired to deceive his wife? They never spoke of things like that.

She saw him remove his watch and lay it on the coffee table. He was slipping off his wedding ring when she stopped him. "No, Ben, I don't want to forget. There's too much at stake. I can't bury my contempt for Lyman and what he's done. You can talk to him if you like, but you have your own battles to fight. This film is my battle and I'm going to talk to him myself."

"It's a mistake, Jess. There's nothing you can do. Please, we haven't much time."

Rising from the couch, she walked to the hallway and stood there waiting. He followed and took her in his arms.

"No," she said. "Not tonight, Ben." She did not want to punish him, or herself. She was very close to tears.

"Do you really want me to go? This has never happened before."

"I know. But this morning when I learned what Lyman had done, I felt like a whore. I don't want to feel that way with you."

NINETEEN

*I*n the countless clashes with Lyman Ellis in the past, Ben had always been her champion, a surrogate warrior stepping into the arena to wage her battles. And because of his love for her and because he was a man of principle, he had voiced her concerns with passion and clarity. This time she was determined to speak for herself, to fight her own battles; but sitting in her office waiting for a summons from Monica, Jessica was beginning to regret her decision. She wanted to be calm and deliberate when she saw Lyman. She had, in fact, dressed with special care that morning. Now she felt wilted, almost breathless. And disloyal. But she knew there were things she could say that Ben could not. For she was no more important to Lyman than the bored waitress in the cafeteria, as insignificant as the security guard in the lobby. She was dispensable, which gave her the freedom to speak.

In the aftermath of yesterday's disaster, Ann and Jeff had taken the day off. Ben, she knew, had left the office early, and without them Jessica felt lonely and unsupported. There seemed to be nothing to do but return the serene gaze of Robert Redford, frozen forever on the poster tacked defiantly to the back of the door. Remembering Max, she took the spindly cactus from its hiding place in her desk drawer and set it on the window sill. Then, glancing around the office, she experienced a shiver of fear, the same fear that had infected the other producers at yesterday's meeting. Lyman had the power to do more than cancel her film; he could fire her. And she loved her job. She even loved this cluttered cubicle of an office. The station was home. Jeff, Ann, Ben, and all the other people who worked with her had become her family. With a word, a gesture, Lyman could snatch it all away. But wouldn't that be preferable to being engulfed by the slowly rising waters of his autocratic control, like someone moving from floor to floor in a flooded house until the entire structure collapses and is swept away?

No, she had to speak, to defend her film, whatever the consequences. For if she saw the station as her home, she could also see that Lyman was relegating her to the nursery, allowed to play with cameras and other grown-up toys until she became too bold, too brash, spoke a truth or made a demand that embarrassed her elders. And with that thought, her resolve was renewed. She would not be treated like a child. And unlike the people she always sought to capture in her films, she would not be a victim.

The phone jangled, startling her. "Miss Lenhart," Monica said crisply, "Mr. Ellis has made room in his schedule to see you for a few minutes at three-thirty. Please try to be on time."

Of course, Lyman would make her wait. Even before the fight began, he had won the first round.

"Come in, Jessica." Closing the financial report he had been reading, Lyman rose to greet her and extended his hand. She took it. As she sat down, she noticed the wall of shiny plaques, which seemed tarnished now in her eyes, and the sinewy Giacometti sculpture that would be the only witness to this conversation.

"I know why you're here," Lyman said, easing himself into the chair facing her. "I spoke to Ben earlier today and I can understand why all of you must be unhappy with the delay in the documentary schedule. But I had absolutely no choice. The Vivaldi concerts are being broadcast live, and when the money became available, I felt it was a cultural opportunity I couldn't refuse. Good films, like fine wines, improve with age, Jessica. They can be shown any time."

"Not mine, Lyman," she said.

"Ah, then you've come to talk about your own film. Isn't that rather self-serving? But I'll tell you exactly what I told Ben this morning. The series has *not* been canceled. All your films will air next year. And Ben made a very eloquent plea for a bigger budget, including money to hire someone to replace Larry Higby, which I promised I would take up with the board at the appropriate time."

"That's wonderful," Jessica said, realizing that Ben must already have struck his own deal with Lyman. But she was in no mood to accept his crumbs. "My film can't wait five months. It has to air as soon as possible. I've looked at the September rundown, and it wouldn't be difficult to preempt an hour."

Lyman cocked his head. "But if I did that for you, I would

have to do it for everyone. I must be even-handed about this."

"I'm not asking for a special favor. The other films are not about a dangerous drug that's ready to go on the market. There are cases against it in the English courts. Both TML and McCampbell are fighting legal action here. And even the FDA has cracked its usual wall of silence . . ."

"Splendid, Jessica," Lyman interrupted. "You must be pleased. Your films don't usually bring such quick results."

"The film hasn't been shown," she said impatiently, indifferent to his insult.

"And you want some of the credit, the glory, is that it? Well, I can understand that."

"No, Lyman, you don't understand. It may take months before the drug is finally banned. People must be warned now. There will be stories in the papers eventually, but they won't have the same impact as a film seen by millions."

"It's possible that you may have a slightly exaggerated notion of the size of your audience."

"Perhaps I do, but that's not the point. The film is finished, ready to air. We'll have the story long before the papers."

"Yes, I know all about you journalists and your eternal quest for scoops. Ben tells me you've made a very good film, Jessica, but you may only think it's finished. If, as you say, cases against the drug are still pending, then it hasn't yet been proved dangerous, and your film could be both premature and potentially defamatory."

"My film is part of the proof, Lyman. I've uncovered evidence of negligence, deception, and possibly even criminal conspiracy between the drug company and the testing lab."

"But are you sure you're right? Let me make a suggestion. Follow these court cases, conduct more interviews with the people involved on both sides, include the trial, the jury coming back with a verdict. Then you'll have the whole story and, incidentally, a very dramatic ending."

"The film is an investigative report, not a historical perspective."

"But surely you want to make it a film that will stand up to time, one that will last? Fortunately, you can do that now. You're over budget as it is, but I can make more money available to you to produce a truly memorable film."

He was fencing, she knew, thrusting with praise, parrying with insults and insinuations, lunging with dollars. She couldn't help admiring his skill even while she was disgusted by his tactics. But they were circling the central issue and she would not leave without saying what had to be said. "Money, that's really what this is all about, isn't it, Lyman? The TML grant."

He smoothed his hair, rearranged his legs. "I'm not sure I know what you mean to imply."

"I'm implying that this film has been a problem for you from the start."

"Did Ben tell you that?"

"He didn't have to. Why do you think Arnie Sultan has followed every move I've made for the last three months? And if TML has been harassing me, I can only imagine what they've demanded of you."

"For a woman who works in reality programming, you have a very creative imagination, Jessica."

"There's no other explanation for what you've done. The rest of the films are harmless: another ghetto rhapsody from Seiden, Higby's Wyoming shepherds. Even Tarr's tirade against labor unions is a safe enough subject. But you had to cancel them all because it was my film you were after. You know it won't air, Lyman. Ever. Wasn't that the price tag attached to the TML grant? And where did the two million for the Vivaldi series come from? Did TML pay for that too?"

Lyman drew in his breath sharply. "I'll pretend I didn't hear that, Jessica. It would be foolish for anyone to make such an insinuation. And if that's all you've come to say to me, our conversation is over."

"No, it's not." She had found her voice. "What do you think will happen when people find out about this? Don't you see the implications? You're destroying the independence and integrity this station is supposed to represent. Your own reputation will be destroyed."

Inexplicably, Lyman began to smile. "Your concern for the station and my reputation is touching. It has the same zeal and passion I've admired in your films. I thought at first you might be threatening me."

"*You* are the threat," Jessica said angrily.

"Spare me, please," Lyman said in a tone of boredom, glancing at his watch. "Now, if you'll excuse me. I have another appointment, and you have a great deal of work to do on your film. Perhaps you ought to get started."

It was useless. She had been unable to touch, even to scratch his impenetrable veneer. His composure remained unruffled, his expression tolerant. Chastened, she could return to the nursery and play with his toys. "No, Lyman," she said, her anger sharpened now by frustration. "I can't and I won't. Not any more. I'm leaving."

At last there was a reaction. Lyman's eyebrows arched in skepticism. "You may think that's very heroic. I think it's rather foolish and unnecessary."

"You've left me no alternative."

"Have you discussed this with Ben? He's very fond of you, I know. I'm sure when you talk this over with him, he'll find some way to make you change your mind."

She recoiled at the smirk that came over his face. "This has nothing to do with Ben."

"It won't be easy to find another job, Jessica. Admirable as your talents are, there aren't very many stations that can utilize them. We all say things we don't mean in the heat of the moment."

"I mean it," she said. She rose and looked down with contempt at his pad of silver hair, the silver-gray of his perfectly tailored suit. "I won't make another film for you to kill. I won't set up another group of people for disappointment. I can't watch you patronize the other producers and walk all over Ben. He doesn't deserve it. But I think I know why you'd like me to stay, and that makes me happy to leave."

"It's final, then," Lyman said with a sigh. "But television may not be the right place for you after all. You work for a few months, spend a few thousand dollars on one film you think is of monumental significance. And perhaps that's your gift. But this station is not in the business of changing the world. Television is merely a reflection. It has eyes and ears . . ."

"But no mind and no heart. I've heard your philosophy of media before."

"Then perhaps you should find some other place to lead your crusades. I can only wish you good luck."

He was standing beside her now, his hand extended again. She ignored it. "There's one more question I'd like to ask. Would you permit me to take my film to another station?"

"You know that's impossible. It's not *your* film."

She turned away from him and started for the door.

"Naturally you'll receive the usual credit when it's aired, even if someone else has to finish it," Lyman said. "And you may win another award, Jessica. The scenes with the boy in London were very affecting."

"Affecting?" She had opened the door, but now she closed it and wheeled around to face him. In his last-minute attempt to leave her with an impression of his generosity and goodwill, he had made his only mistake. "Then you've seen it," she said. "It *was* you who snuck into the editing room in the middle of the night. You saw what that drug can do and still you killed my film."

He was shaken by the ferocity of her words. "I had every right to see it. I'm in charge of this station."

"You are a snake!" Jessica cried. "Because of you, that 'affecting' little boy will be dragged through countless courtrooms, put on public display as if he were some kind of freak. And who knows how many more children there are just like him? Who knows how many more there will be because of you!"

"Get out of this office," Lyman hissed. "Get out of my station."

"It's only yours for the moment, Lyman. You may have killed a film and saved your grant. But there's another story just as important as the side effects of Styralon that you won't be able to kill. It's the story of this place and what you've done to it: the terrible, toxic side effects of working here."

She took a last look at Lyman Ellis and saw him only as a small, insubstantial shadow of a man as she walked out and slammed the door.

Pale, trembling, her eyes streaming with tears, she poked through the disorder of her office like someone sorting out the possessions of a person who has just died. What could she take with her, what should she leave behind? The tapes of her films, the books, the magazines, they belonged to the station. But the transcripts were available to anyone and she pulled them from the files and crammed them into her tote bag. She would have only words, but that was enough. The faces behind the words, the images, she would remember forever.

God, what had she done? She had meant only to make a last eloquent plea for her film, not to leave a job she adored. But she realized now that Lyman had been playing a double game, urging her to stay and at the same time goading her into quitting. Had she really called him a snake? She was delighted with that, but she could hardly remember what else she had said. And all of it was wasted on Lyman. Why hadn't she fought him as Ben so often did, with patience, stealth, little sacrifices of pride and principle? And if total victory was impossible, why hadn't she been able to compromise? Where was her pragmatism, the cynicism that matched her idealism? Was she so right, so perfect? In the white light of Ben's love and protection, she had been made to think so.

She could imagine Ben's face when he heard what she had done, and the thought of his reaction saddened her as much as the loss of her job. It wouldn't be easy to find another one; she knew the reach of Lyman's tentacles. For the fleeting pleasure of telling Lyman nothing more than he clearly knew about himself, she might have to sacrifice much more than her job. And for a moment, forgetting that Ben had already left the office, she considered running down the hall to see him, asking him to intercede. In the familiar comfort of his arms, she would stop crying, and in the small, private world they had created, she would feel safe again.

No, even if Ben were there, she couldn't do that. She felt like a tightrope walker working for the first time without a net. But she decided to write Ben a formal letter of resignation and then they would talk, continue to have what they had, perhaps even more. In time they would laugh about all this. They would survive.

It was odd, she thought. For five years from her place behind the camera, she had urged her subjects to vent their frustration and rage, cry out against the indignities and injustice in their lives—but please, don't call me by name. Now, suddenly, the camera had turned on her, the lights blinded her eyes, and she comprehended the enormity of what she had asked them to do, what she herself had done. Heroic and perhaps futile in the end, but necessary.

No longer crying, she packed a pair of boots, the forgotten survivors of a late winter snowstorm, in her bag, tucked her umbrella under her arm. There was only one more thing she wanted to take with her: Max, the feeble symbol of her first rebellion against Lyman Ellis and all he stood for. Hidden in a desk drawer at night, over-watered and over-protected by day, it was a miracle that it was still alive.

No one saw her leave. At that hour on a Friday afternoon the hallways were deserted, the elevator empty. The security guard in the lobby gave her a curious stare as she struggled through the revolving door to the street. There, standing on a corner, an umbrella in one hand and a bulging tote bag topped by winter boots and a tropical cactus in the other, she looked more like a refugee from an institution than a filmmaker who had just lost her job. She raised the umbrella skyward to flag a taxi.

Lost her job? She was leaving much more than that.

The weekend seemed interminable, a prolonged pause for breath, and Jessica felt like someone in a theater audience milling aimlessly around the lobby during intermission, waiting somewhat expectantly, somewhat reluctantly, for the next act to begin. She was the only one who knew what she had done. And needing some confirmation of the rightness of her act, some reassurance, she decided to call Ben. But she had to ask the operator for his number, and each time she began to dial it, she stopped. In four years she had never called him at home. She could not do it now.

She had never called Doug at home either. And looking up his number in the phone book, she was struck by a new and totally unpleasant revelation. She knew the numbers of everyone in her life except the two men with whom she had been more intimate than anyone else. She was relieved when there was no answer. What did she want from him: sympathy, congratulations? She didn't know, just as she wasn't certain what direction her emotions should take. They shifted, as did her image of herself. Saturday morning she was still the armor-clad Joan of Arc undaunted in defeat; by evening she was the naive country maid who had carelessly lit the fires of her own funeral pyre.

On Sunday she called her mother and Beryl took the news as calmly as if her daughter were calling to announce she had lost a treasured but replaceable silk scarf. "Well, darling, it's for the best, I'm sure. You'll find a much better job, one that won't take so much out of you. Meanwhile, you've got to be good to yourself. Why don't you come home for a while? Or you could plan a trip."

Jessica enjoyed the irony of being a modern-day heroine packed off to Europe to lick her wounds for reasons other than an affair of the heart.

"Maybe I could join you," Beryl continued. "Although goodness knows, with things the way they are, bombs exploding everywhere, terrorists blowing up airplanes, I don't know where we could go."

Beryl and her endless warnings. Jessica remembered the caveats of her childhood, catastrophes that lurked around every corner: oceans that would swallow her up, lightning bolts that would strike her if she played in the rain, mosquito bites that turned malignant, bees that stung, plugs that electrocuted, strange men, vicious dogs, terminal diseases that contaminated toilet seats. In Beryl's mind, it was a barbed-wire world, a landscape studded with exploding mines that her daughter must negotiate with caution, and Jessica had laughed at her mother's warnings in the past. But today it seemed that Beryl had been right after all.

"Or I have an even better idea," she went on. "I have just one social engagement next week. It's a surprise party for Roger Lyons who's getting out of the hospital after open heart surgery and I don't want to miss it."

"A surprise party?" Jessica laughed. "Mother, do you think that's wise?"

"After that I'm coming to New York. We can shop, go to the theater. This is no time for you to be alone." Leaving the station also meant leaving Ben Nevins, and although she didn't say it, that was clearly a piece of good news that Beryl wished to see for herself. And celebrate.

She called Wanda, whose first thought was not of Jessica but how she would tell Mel. "It's bad enough every time he sees the paper, or gets a call from that damn office," she said, "but your film *and* your job? I'll have to figure out some way to break it to him gently. How are you taking it?"

"I'm still furious, but also a little scared."

"I know the feeling. When are you and my beloved husband going to learn it's a wicked world and there isn't a damn thing you can do about it?"

With Monday morning and the prospect of an empty day, empty weeks, before her, Jessica realized that just as she and Ben had woven a net of rituals around their love, the ritual she knew best, work, had been ripped apart. She had nothing to do, no place to go, and the self-righteousness that had sustained her throughout the weekend was now tinged with self-pity. She read the paper from first page to last, including the shipping news. Wandering through her apartment, she considered cleaning out closets, straightening drawers. She saw Max on a window sill, bathed in unfamiliar early morning sunlight. It looked wretched. Accustomed to its own rituals, nights in a desk drawer and days in the chill of the air-conditioned office, Max, too, was a casualty of displacement.

Then the phone began to ring and didn't stop. Doug, the first to call, tried to make light of it. "Mel told me. He was mad as hell and says he won't go to his grave happy until he gets your friend Lyman Ellis." Then his tone changed to one of concern. "Did you have to quit?"

"No. Yes, yes I did."

"And what about the film? I'd like to give it to the federal prosecutor. Any chance I can get a copy?"

"No chance, short of breaking into Lyman's safe. But I've got a transcript, all my notes and files. You can have those."

"Great. That'll help. I think I can prove Styralon is dangerous, but I can't prove McCampbell knew it. And that means even if the drug is banned, they could walk away from it with clean hands. What are you going to do?"

"Start looking for a new job, I guess. But at the moment I feel strangely indolent."

"Enjoy it. You've earned it. Let's have dinner and we can celebrate the rude awakening of Alice in Wonderland."

After he hung up, Jessica realized it was not only indolence she felt but powerlessness. There was nothing more she could do to stop Styralon. She was a preacher without a pulpit, a politician without a soapbox, a crusader without a cause.

The next call was from Ann. "Jessie, we love you! And you are missed. This whole place is in an uproar. What happened? Did you hit Lyman over the head with the Giacometti?"

"No. We had words and I quit. How did you find out?"

"Ben told us. There was a memo on his desk this morning

from Lyman which read, and I quote, 'At her request, Jessica Lenhart's employment by this station has been terminated, effective immediately.' And some minion from the executive floor walked in here, snooped around, and asked if you had removed any station property. I didn't tell him about Max."

Then Jeff was on the line. "You're beautiful, baby. Beautiful, but dumb. If you had let Lyman fire you, we would have something to protest. Not to mention how much easier it would be for you to get unemployment. Now all we can do is leak the story to the press. Higby is calling the Committee for the Rights of Investigative Journalists, the Peter Zenger group. Even Tarr is sore at Lyman. Is there something I can do?"

"I hesitate to ask, Jeff, but can you get me a copy of the film?"

"In other words commit criminal trespass, burglary, copyright infringement, and professional suicide?"

"Well, yes."

"You got it, baby."

The phone rang again almost immediately. It was Ben. "I've been trying to reach you all morning. Have you had the phone off the hook?"

"People have been calling," she said.

"Jess, what in the name of God have you done? Lyman won't see me. The producers are walking around with fire in their eyes. Don't you realize you've given Lyman the best possible reason to kill your film forever?"

"It doesn't matter. He never had any intention of letting it air."

"What did you say to him?"

"I don't remember all of it. Things I've wanted to say for years."

"Why the hell didn't you talk to me first?"

"I did, Ben. I tried."

"But why did you have to quit?"

"Ben, please. When I went in there, I didn't plan to quit. It just happened. I know you're angry and I suppose I did it all wrong, but at least I did it. Can't you be a little proud of me for that?"

"You're forgetting one thing, Jess. I love you. What will happen to us?"

Jessica felt a tiny shudder of apprehension. It was the same question she had asked herself, and she was about to tell him that perhaps they could have even more, that their time together could be different, enriched. But instead she said, "I don't know, Ben. Whatever we want to happen."

Friends called when they heard the news, suggesting lunch, shopping excursions, trips to museums. Activities she had crammed into a few weekend hours could now consume whole days. Kate invited her to another ethnic evening. Her mother phoned every day asking if she was all right, if she needed money. But then, the calls stopped, and Jessica was confronted with the necessity of filling time she never had, like the poor man who wins a million dollars in a lottery and doesn't know how to spend it. It was foolish to try to find a job in August; that could wait until after Labor Day and she thought she would enjoy her idleness. But after only a few days, what was meant to be a light indulgence had turned into a lifeless gloom and she felt as if she were slipping into a void.

She did not even have the luxury of leading her own crusade. A brief item about her resignation appeared in the paper under the headline: WPTN PRODUCER QUITS IN SCHEDULE DISPUTE. "Denying rumors," the article went on to say, "that her departure was in any way connected with unwarranted censorship of her films, Lyman Ellis, the chairman of the board at WPTN, said he accepted Miss Lenhart's resignation with regret." No mention of Styralon, the TML grant, or the sudden influx of Vivaldi dollars. Her stand on principle had been made to seem mere petulance. Lyman's tentacles were very long indeed.

She and Ben had arranged their usual Thursday evening, and that afternoon, a messenger delivered a box of coral roses to her apartment. For Jessica, as she arranged them in the vase in her bedroom, it seemed to be an act of remembrance, not love. Getting ready to meet him, watching the water of her bath circle down the drain, she remembered something she had said to Kate a long time ago. Ben was the earth and the moon, her love and her work pulling together to create the tides of her life, and without both, she feared she would become a body of still water. She lacked engagement, but the other things she missed were curiously insignificant: Ann's saucer-blue eyes, Jeff's unlit pipe, Irv Seiden's goatee. And because she needed an adversary, she even missed Lyman Ellis. She joked about her loss, telling Wanda only that morning, "I had to buy stamps for the first time in years and they cost a fortune. You don't happen to know where I can get them at a discount?" But there was no one to tell of her fear of an even greater loss: the sun and the moon moving inexorably toward a total eclipse.

Ben was wearing the blue-checked shirt and blazer he always wore on Thursdays. "Do you remember the first time we had dinner?" he asked, reaching for her hand across the table in the quiet restaurant they had chosen. "We'd just quarreled with Lyman about one of your films. In a funny way, that bastard brought us together."

She remembered that night, her confusion, her tears, and how she had welcomed the shelter of his arms. He was offering the same thing to her now.

"I assume you saw your name in the paper," he said.

"Higby did that. He figured he didn't have anything to lose, but the reporter went to Lyman to check and that's the story they printed."

He ordered a bottle of Sancerre and over dinner gossiped about the station. "There's a rumor that Scott and Maureen were going to get married, but they went for a blood test and discovered they didn't have any."

Jessica laughed, knowing that Ben was making fun of her old world so that her sudden removal from it would seem less painful. He went on about the budget, the new fall shows, talking of all the things that had consumed so much of their time in the past, and she felt as if she were reading a newspaper from a land she had loved and had somehow betrayed, a country from which she had been banished in permanent exile.

"Ann is leaving, too. Higby is taking her with him. As a matter of fact, the future of the whole unit looks bleak. I called off the meeting. Tarr and Seiden don't have any new ideas. And with only two producers left, Lyman has a perfect excuse to kill the unit."

"Has he said anything about me?"

"Cool, gray silence. But I think I can persuade him to let you come back, Jess. You've made your point. Please, won't you let me try?"

As much as she missed her job, as much as she wanted to stitch up the torn fabric of her life, she had never considered that. "No, Ben, it's impossible. Lyman would never forgive me for what I said to him. And even if he let me come back, he would only find some other way to destroy my work. Fight for the unit, for new producers, for a budget, but don't fight for me."

"I'm fighting for us, Jess. I'm afraid to tell you how much I miss you. I used to run to work every morning because I knew you'd be there. Now the office is empty, and I go to work like everyone else, grudging, plodding. Hours put in, nothing more. Without seeing you every day, my life is empty."

She did not doubt his words. She only doubted that he understood the emptiness of her life. "You know I can't go back. Please, let's talk about something else."

They tried. Wars, revolutions, politics, the state of the nation, the state of the world, but their conversation seemed artificial, strained, as if they were strangers killing time on a long transatlantic flight. Killing time, they who had conspired to steal or borrow it for four years, spending it like a miser spends his gold? Working together, common ground had been everywhere. Now it eluded them and they could speak only of impersonal things, for they knew so little of the parts of their lives they had never shared. Those were subjects that had always been banned from their small, perfect world like disreputable applicants to an exclusive club. They were its only members, and exclusion had become isolation, even from each other.

Back in her apartment, Jessica hoped that kissing and touching would restore the intimate connections between them. And then they could talk, building from the solid foundation of their love a new structure to accommodate new needs, new ceremonies to replace the rites and rituals that were no longer relevant, a new litany, a new language, a new timetable in place of the old.

But the act of love was intense and quickly terminated, and before she could find the words she wanted to speak, he was in the shower. She went to the kitchen to make coffee and brought it to him in the living room, where, buttoning his shirt and knotting his tie, he looked too fresh, too unwrinkled for a man who would have to pretend he had been working since morning. He smelled of her soap. Had Sara never noticed that?

"I hate this," he said. "Getting up and going home. Four years and it never gets easier. But it won't have to be that way now, Jess. It won't have to be just Thursdays. I can come here in the afternoon. We'll have time to do things we've never done before."

She nodded her head, feigning agreement, feeling numb.

In the hallway he kissed her tenderly, his mouth as sweet as lemons. A morning mouth. "Jess, the Ritz?"

"Of course it was," she said.

"No, will be. I have to make a trip to Paris for the station in October and I want you to come. The real Ritz. It's been a myth too long."

They embraced and the attaché case bouncing lightly on her back felt like brutal blows.

Then he was gone. And her mind was filled with a rush of unpleasant images: strangers on a plane, restricted clubs, a lifetime of Thursdays with an occasional afternoon. And the Ritz, even in reality no more than a tawdry motel. She felt soiled, a woman living in the shadows of a back street, waiting, expected to want only what he wanted.

She began to cry as she took the coffee cups back to the kitchen and rinsed them in the sink. She was still crying as she straightened the rumpled bed, smoothing away the last impressions of his presence. Her eyes dimmed by tears, she could no longer see what it was she wanted, no longer knew what she had wished to secure. And like the guerrilla fighter suddenly stripped of belief in the rightness of her goal, she was bereft of strategy.

TWENTY

*T*here was nothing she could do with her sadness. For days it filled her thoughts, drained her body of energy, sapped her spirits, until she finally decided to attack it, as if it were an idea for a film. Admitting that her guile had always been as essential as her intellect, she struggled to arrive at a scheme, even a lie, to coax herself out of her depression. But she could find nothing to fill her empty days, and the memory of her last night with Ben would not budge from her mind. Feeling strangely impotent, she realized her own cunning was not enough. She had to talk to someone.

Waiting impatiently at a traffic light a block from Kate's

apartment building, she tried to ignore the blistering heat. In August, Freudians and Jungians alike abandoned the island of Manhattan, retreating to islands of their own, leaving the city a hotbed of free-floating angst. But fortunately, Paul and Kate always saved their vacation for the splendid days of October. Her forehead drenched with perspiration, Jessica remembered the chilly fall day when she had first gone to see Kate to speak of her father's death, her own grief obscured by her mother's overwhelming sense of loss. She had never imagined she would return with a loss of her own.

A woman with weary eyes wheeled a baby carriage toward the park, followed by another child pedaling his tricycle with fierce concentration. Jessica stepped aside with a sympathetic smile and thought it strange that she had never wanted that. Considering the disarray of her life, it was odd that she could find comfort in what she had chosen *not* to be, solace in negations.

In the elevator, she considered what she would say to Kate. What did she want from her, mothering? She could hear Beryl's voice soothing away her childish hurts, could taste the special tea her mother brewed when she was ill. Beryl's love had always blossomed with her daughter's slightest discomfort, as if a microscopic virus was a medical emergency, a playground fight an international incident. Tears, sniffles, scraped knees and elbows—Beryl had waged war on them all with tea and kisses. What would Kate offer? She was a friend, a friend who had always disapproved of Ben.

Kate was standing in the doorway, arms outstretched in welcome. Ignoring the backroom that resonated with the outdated terms of their past relationship, she led Jessica into the living room. Without the usual crowd that congregated at her parties, it looked large, almost barren. "Sit down," Kate said. "Have you been walking in this heat? You must be exhausted. Let me fix you something. A glass of iced tea?"

Jessica enjoyed the irony of her offer, but before she had time to arrange her thoughts, Kate had returned. "Paul sends his love. He thinks what you did was very brave. And he says there are more than a few people in the world who share your opinion of Lyman Ellis. But heroes, unfortunately, seldom make headlines."

"I don't feel very heroic. What have I accomplished? The film will never be shown. Lyman will never change. And I'm out of a job." Jessica sipped her tea, trying to remain calm. "All that was inevitable, I suppose. But something else is happening and I don't even know what it is."

Kate perceived her meaning instantly. "You and Ben?" she said. "Perhaps that was inevitable, too."

"I've wanted things to be different between us for a long time. Ben and I have lived in a vacuum for years. Outside the station, it's always been just the two of us, feeding off each other. When I left, I thought all that would change. We could be ourselves, share more of our lives. And things *are* different. But not the way I hoped. Our love is a little tarnished, a little strained. And I don't want to believe it can't survive anywhere, flourish in the open air. How can love be a creature of context?"

"Does Ben feel that way?"

"I don't think so."

"Then he doesn't want to end it?"

"End it? He wants more, too, but more of the same—with a few added enhancements. Matinees."

"I see," Kate said impassively. "Have you talked about this?"

"No. I'm not sure he would understand."

"Then have you tried to see it from his point of view?"

Looking at her friend sitting placidly before her, Jessica felt this was a time for jagged edges, tense bodies, not for the physical grace or cool dispassionate style that was Kate's trademark. Nor was she intrigued by the notion of Kate playing devil's advocate. She could have accepted consolation or even criticism; she had not expected Kate asking her to be fair.

"I'm sure Ben thinks you're the one who's changing things, destroying what you had. And he probably thinks you've acted childishly."

"And you, Kate, with your Ph.D. in infantilism, what do you think? Am I being a child?"

Kate ignored her sarcasm. "I'm not sure. I know how much you love your work, and you've told me for years how much you care about this man. But I sense that you feel he's somehow failed you. He wasn't able to prevent Lyman Ellis from keeping your film off the air. And now that you're not working, he isn't able to fill that void in your life. But has he really changed? I doubt it. Perhaps it's you who have changed."

Jessica felt the chill of the air conditioner on the back of her neck, the chill that was spreading between her friend and herself. "You're defending him?"

"No. I'm just saying that no one is perfect. Every child learns and must accept that about his parents."

"Parents? Then you *do* think I'm a child," Jessica said with resentment.

"I'm speaking as your friend," Kate said calmly, "not an analyst."

"Then tell me what to do. Ben wants me to come back to the station. How can I? How could he even ask?"

"Because he may be frightened for you."

"And what are his fears for me?"

"That he'll lose you, for one thing."

"That's his fear for himself. What are his fears for me?"

"That you may not be able to find another job. That

you're giving up everything to make a small moral point."

"A small moral point?" Jessica echoed Kate's words indignantly. "He couldn't believe that. He knows as much about that drug as I do. I told him about the man who broke into your apartment, and that Lyman would have even used our personal relationship against us to stop the film if another convenient reason hadn't come along. But let's assume he could persuade Lyman to take me back, and I went back, knowing that every important idea I had, every important film I made, would always be hostage to Lyman's power. Who would I be?"

"You would still be you. I'm sure Ben would tell you that."

"Forget Ben for a moment," she said with irritation. "What would I have?"

"Him," Kate said simply. "I can't let you forget that."

"Or the tiny piece of him that he shares with me, as you've reminded me so often. You've prodded and needled me about having a fragmented love. But now suddenly you approve of it. You want me to go back."

"I didn't say that. What I'm saying is that you may lose too much all at once. And never know why. You've got to salvage something for yourself. Martyrdom isn't cheap, Jessica. It's always an exquisite but painfully brief moment. And at the risk of slipping into my professional persona—martyrdom, masochism, sometimes it's hard to tell them apart, even in saints."

"So now I'm a masochistic child," Jessica said ruefully. "I'm just trying to figure out what's happening to Ben and me. I don't understand him any more. I don't understand how he deals with Lyman every day, how he can make peace with that kind of compromise. And what kind of peace, what kind of compromise has he made with his wife? I don't understand that after so many years he doesn't really know me."

Kate leaned forward, her strong hands in a gesture of appeal. "But what has he done that he's never done before? He didn't cancel your film. Lyman did. And he's not responsible for the loss of your job. You did that. These things have happened around him, not because of him. And the bargains he has struck with Lyman, the compromises he has made with his wife, were not only for himself. They were for you as well. And they never troubled you in the past. Imagine how he must feel now that you've left the station and he fears you may leave him, too. Hurt, abandonment, and pain no less than yours because he may be more needful of you than you are of him."

Kate was like quicksilver, changing tactics, shifting positions, making Jessica feel like an empty bottle tossed about in the tide. "But I *do* need him," she said. "You know what we had, what we were. He was my life."

"Yes, I know. Do you remember the story you once told me about the beach umbrella? That was your life. You made the station your safe, benevolent world, filled with a love so strong you could accept only pieces and parts of Ben. No one can live under a beach umbrella forever, Jessica. But then, no one should kick it over and run recklessly into the sea."

In the backroom, the phone rang and the sound of Kate's disembodied voice on the answering machine added a surrealistic tone to the dark reality spread out between them. Jessica thought of the station and its machines: humming cameras, crackling tape recorders, miles and miles of a film of her life flickering across the Moviola. Where was Jeff to cut and splice each scene to make it fit? Why wouldn't Kate tell her how to edit her life?

"Give it time, Jessica," she said. "Perhaps you and Ben can get used to a new arrangement, even without the station. Perhaps it will lead to something better for both of you. You've told me that's what you want."

"I'm not sure what I want."

Kate's perceptions were quick, her intuition unerring. "Then is there something else?" she said. "Someone else?"

Color rushed to Jessica's face. Kate's words shocked her, as if she had picked up a book she thought she had never read and then found a paragraph, a line that brought it all back to her in an instant. "There is," she began slowly. "Or there was. Do you remember the lawyer I told you about? We went to London to film the family whose child had been damaged by Styralon. I don't know how it happened. But it did. We spent a night together and I hated myself for it. I hated him, too. We've fought from the first moment we met. We still fight. And I thought I could forget the whole thing. But I can't. He lingers in my mind like the one good song from a show that closed on opening night. He won't let me forget."

"Then you still see him?"

"Not often. And now that my film has been canceled, I'll probably never see him again."

"When are you seeing Ben?"

"Thursday, of course," Jessica said, lowering her head and closing her eyes.

"I know how you feel," Kate said. "Sometimes it's easier to change the world than change ourselves."

Damn Kate. But of course she was right. Ben was no different. It was she who was changing. Thinking only of her loss, she had not considered that his was as great, his need for her now even greater than before. Leaving Kate's apartment, Jessica walked in a purple twilight through the muggy city streets all the way to the Village, trying to think things out, hoping to make herself tired. Heat lightning flashed through the sky, the sound of thunder rumbled in the distance but the storm would not break. And Jessica's sadness was now compounded by the admission of a long repressed truth. She and Ben *were* creatures of context; she *had* settled for fragments, crumbs. But at last she had a new strategy, a new goal. It was absurd that she hadn't realized it before. It was only necessary to create a new context.

She kicked off her shoes in the hallway of her apartment, collapsed on the couch, too tired to eat, too tired even to sleep, and an absurd vision danced before her eyes: all the organs of the human body, each of a different color—a blue brain, yellow lungs, a red heart—not neatly labeled and arranged as they were on the chart in Dr. Rudnick's laboratory, but stitched together at random like a crazy quilt. Kate was there, Ben and Sara, Lyman, Beryl, Doug, watching attentively as she snipped the stitches, pulled the pieces apart, then tried to sew them up again in some semblance of order.

The sound of the telephone nudged her from a surface sleep. Shaking her head to clear the unsettling dream from her mind, she picked it up. "Yes?"

"Miss Lenhart? Miss Jessica Lenhart?"

Jessica did not recognize the voice.

"This is Madge Barwick. Do you remember me?"

Wide awake now, Jessica said, "Of course. Are you calling from Washington?"

"No, I'm in New York. I received your letter and I'd like to talk to you as soon as possible. It's very important."

"Where are you staying?" Jessica asked. "I can meet you there, or better yet, why don't you come to my apartment?"

"No, I can't do that. There's a small bar near my hotel. Can we meet there tomorrow at four o'clock?"

She gave Jessica the address and then hung up abruptly.

Puzzled, Jessica recalled her impressions of Madge Barwick, fidgeting, fluttery as she told the vague story of her involvement in the government's approval of Styralon. It was a far different story from the one Daniel Bowen told, but in the end she had used the woman's interview sparingly in the film. She was, after all, a small cog on a big, bureaucratic wheel. Still Jessica remembered her clearly, just as she remembered the fleeting expression of apprehension that had crossed her face when she was asked to sign the customary release form at the end of the interview. Jessica had written to tell her the film had been postponed. But that was two weeks ago. She wondered why Madge Barwick wanted to see her now.

Hesitating only for a moment, Jessica again picked up the phone.

"Hello." The voice at the other end of the line was low and slightly querulous.

"Is Mr. Weber there?"

"Who's calling?"

"This is Jessica Lenhart."

"Oh, yes. The lady with the plaque."

Jessica hadn't forgotten that evening, or that voice. "Hello, Bambi."

"Wait a minute."

Then Doug was on the phone. "Jess? Hi."

"I'm sorry to disturb you at home."

"You're not disturbing me. What's up?"

"I just got a call from Madge Barwick. She's in New York and wants to see me tomorrow. I have a funny feeling about it, Doug, and I think you should be there."

At that hour, the small, dark bar was almost empty. A woman was drinking martinis, a poodle curled up around the legs of the stool on which she sat, while the bartender polished glasses and watched a baseball game on television. Doug was already there when Jessica arrived and they took their drinks to a booth in the back. Madge Barwick entered a few moments later, hesitated as if she thought she might be in the wrong place, then approached them.

"You're not alone," she said to Jessica.

"You sounded troubled over the phone, Mrs. Barwick. I thought perhaps Mr. Weber could help."

"May I get you a drink?" Doug asked.

"No, nothing for me," she said with the same fluttery gestures Jessica remembered from Washington. Then she changed her mind. "Well, yes. A small brandy, please."

Dressed in a badly creased linen suit, Madge Barwick was not at all the precise, neatly arranged woman of a few months before. Her round face, framed in reddish-brown curls, was puffy and bloated, and again there was apprehension in her eyes. Sipping brandy, she seemed agitated and unsure of how to proceed. Finally she said, "I'm sorry your film has been postponed, Miss Lenhart. When will it be shown?"

"That's still uncertain," Jessica replied.

"Did I look all right? I hope I didn't seem too silly," she said with an unconvincing attempt at her usual eagerness to please. "I don't really remember what I said."

"You told us what you could recall about Styralon. And you mentioned a meeting with Daniel Bowen."

"Oh, yes. Now I remember. I don't suppose you ever found him?"

"Yes, we did, Mrs. Barwick. His interview is a major part of my film."

The color drained from Madge Barwick's face, leaving only bright red patches of rouge on her cheeks. Her body slumped, her hands were still.

"We know you didn't tell us everything," Jessica said, her voice gentle, unaccusing. "Is that what's troubling you?"

"But I didn't lie," Madge Barwick said with a breathless

urgency. "I mean I thought it wouldn't matter. The drug was safe. Everyone said so; the agency had approved it. And Daniel Bowen had made such wild accusations and demands. He came to see me, you know. I thought he was mad. But how could I tell you that? I felt very sorry for him and was trying to protect him."

Doug reacted with disbelief. "Him or someone else?"

Jessica glanced at him, her expression a request to treat this fragile woman carefully. "We can understand that," she said. "In many ways Dr. Bowen is a very tragic figure. But you told us that no unfavorable reports on Styralon were submitted to you. Dr. Bowen said he gave you that information to you himself."

"And you should have seen it. Clippings from English newspapers, pages ripped out of medical journals, laboratory tests from goodness knows where—he said they were his. Nothing in the proper order, nothing on the proper form. What was I supposed to do with things like that?"

"What did you do?" Jessica asked.

"Well, I certainly couldn't send them through the usual channels, so I didn't. I would have been laughed right out of the agency. But I couldn't ignore them either. So I sent all of Dr. Bowen's information to Chanterelle and asked them to resubmit it to us in the proper form if they thought it was in any way pertinent to Styralon's application for approval."

"Was that the proper thing to do?"

Jessica cut off Doug's question. "What was Chanterelle's reply?"

"There was no formal reply. A friend at Chanterelle called and told me that poor Dr. Bowen was besieged with personal problems. The death of his only son had completely shattered him and his work had suffered because of it. My friend also told me he knew all about the controversy in

England and said it was a tempest in a teapot, the sort of medical dispute that so often surrounds any new drug. His tests, he assured me, had convinced him and everyone at McCampbell that Styralon was absolutely safe."

"Did you ever tell anyone at the agency about your meeting with Dr. Bowen?" Doug asked.

"No," Madge Barwick replied, "I knew my friend was right."

"May I ask the name of your friend?" Jessica asked.

"It doesn't matter. Just someone at Chanterelle I've worked with for several years. A man I know I can trust."

"Are you so sure?" Jessica asked. "Did you ever wonder why Dr. Bowen's signature was on all of Chanterelle's favorable reports when he was so vehemently opposed to the drug? Dr. Bowen told us that he was not permitted to complete his tests on Styralon. No one at McCampbell would listen to him. Chanterelle forced him to retire. He came to your agency, to you, Mrs. Barwick, as a desperate last resort."

"How could I know that?" she cried. "What are you accusing me of? I've done nothing wrong."

"We're not accusing you of anything," Jessica said gently. "But if you feel you've done nothing wrong, why did you ask to see me? You must be relieved that my film has been delayed, particularly if you were afraid Dr. Bowen's story would contradict yours."

"No, no, you don't understand at all. I *wanted* your film to be shown. I hoped it would explain everything. Even if I hadn't told you all I remembered, I thought you would find out the truth."

"The truth," Doug exclaimed. "And just what is the truth?"

All the features on Madge Barwick's face seemed to converge, robbing it of definition. "I thought Styralon was safe. A medical miracle, just like my friend said it was. But I don't know anymore. Now everyone at the agency is talking about it. And there's a trial in England where they claim children have been damaged by the drug."

"We filmed one of those children in London," Jessica said. "He's a very brave little boy."

"Please, don't tell me that." Madge Barwick was crying now, tears running down her cheeks. "I know about your case, too, Mr. Weber. The agency is in an uproar. Tell me, Miss Lenhart, is the drug really dangerous? Does it cause birth defects?"

"It's a hard teratogen. There's no doubt."

"Then it must be banned," Madge Barwick said, regaining control of herself. "Sometimes, the agency moves so slowly. But your film, your film, won't that help? When will it be shown?"

"It will never be shown," Jessica said. "The company that owns McCampbell has been powerful enough to stop it. And I no longer work at the station."

"And if McCampbell wins their appeal," Doug said, "the drug will be put on the market."

"But that can't happen now," Madge Barwick pleaded. "There can't be any more damaged children."

"What about the women in England who've taken the drug already?" Doug said. "And what about the men in this country who conspired to sell it, knowing it was dangerous?"

"Conspired? What do you mean?"

"I'm trying to prove in court that McCampbell and Chanterelle intentionally withheld information from your agency to win approval for Styralon. And that is criminal conspiracy."

Again, Madge Barwick's hands began to flutter. "But that would mean fines, imprisonment. No, I can't believe that anyone, for any reason, would do such a thing."

"I believe that's exactly what did happen," Doug said. "And you can help us prove it. You can tell the court just what you've told us. It doesn't matter now what you said or didn't say on Jessica's film."

Madge Barwick's reaction was immediate. "No, I won't do it. I can't. It was nothing more than an honest mistake. A judgment call, as it frequently is with any new drug. A man's reputation, his business, his whole life shouldn't be destroyed for that."

"Dr. Bowen's life has been destroyed," Jessica said. "The lives of many children and their families in England have been destroyed."

"You don't understand what you're asking me to do."

"I can subpoena you, Mrs. Barwick," Doug said. "Force you to testify."

"Then I'll lie," she said with grim determination in her voice. "I don't care if I lose my job. I don't care what happens to me. I will not betray my friend."

"Don't you think he has betrayed you?" Jessica asked.

Madge Barwick sipped the last of her brandy, considering her reply. "No," she said. "He loves me. We're going to be married. He has a wife, children, and he's giving it all up, giving up a whole life for me. And I will not say anything against him. Don't you see, Miss Lenhart? I'm not young. I'm not beautiful . . ."

"Then you don't give a damn about stopping this drug," Doug finally exploded. "What kind of woman are you?"

Jessica frowned at him, again trying to silence his anger. "But you must know that's wrong."

"Perhaps. But it's an imperfect world, Miss Lenhart, and you're imperfect, too. Oh yes, you're young and you're beautiful, but there are things you will do one day, things you may have already done, in the name of love. So please, save your scorn."

Late afternoon sunlight blinded them momentarily as they left the bar. In numb, solemn silence, they walked the few blocks to Fifth Avenue and crossed into Central Park where they thought the air would be clearer, the world less imperfect. "You feel sorry for her, don't you, Jess?" Doug said. "He used her and she's so desperate that she's still protecting him."

"And the him, of course, is Karl Engle?"

"Probably, but who knows? It could be anyone at Chanterelle. They were all in on it. You should have been tougher on her."

"Why? You have your case now, don't you? That's all that really matters. Besides, I'm beyond being tough on anyone. Do you remember you once asked me what happened to the people I filmed, the lives I disrupted, and I said I never had time to think about that. I do now. The Styralon story was supposed to be so simple—greed, arrogance, a shining example of the corrosive power of big business and the failure of government to control it."

"Money and power."

"Those are abstractions. But everyone I filmed who was damaged by the drug—the Harcents, the Bowens, even Madge Barwick. They're people, and I'll never forget them."

Near the carousel, the park suddenly took on the atmosphere of a small town invaded by a carnival, with ice cream carts and hotdog stands clustered together under brightly striped awnings. Children clutching balloons and cones of pink cotton candy waited impatiently in line for a ride on the carousel, which was, for some reason, empty, its carved horses prancing up and down, around and around, without riders, without music. Pausing to watch, Jessica thought of herself. And like the carved horses, she felt that she, too, was moving around in silent circles. She remembered the rainy night when she and Doug had passed the toy store window; she remembered the swings and slide in the Harcents' tiny garden playground. Inevitably, when they were together, they seemed to be surrounded by the symbols of childhood. Yet he stirred pools of feeling in her that were not at all childlike.

Deeper in the park, they followed a wooded walk and found an empty bench. "You've been hurt by Styralon, too, Jess. Your film was killed. You lost your job. I'm sorry."

"But that wasn't your fault. You didn't want me to make the film, remember? And you were the one who told me what my business is really like the first time we met."

"I didn't want to be right. Like the Constitution, it was nice to know you were there."

He had removed his tie, unbuttoned his collar, and in the shadowy light his dark eyes were barely visible. Sitting next to him, she wondered, When it had happened? When had he ceased to be a carping critic, an adversary who assaulted her profession, her motives, her integrity? Had it been a gradual or a sudden transformation? He was a man of edges and angles, but now he looked smoother, softer, soft enough to trust with a memory. It was a story she had never told anyone, not Kate, not even Ben. "I'm not sorry about the job," she said. "Not really. It had to happen eventually. The sad thing is that it happened before. And I tried to forget it, block it from my mind. I've closed my eyes to so much."

"You mean at the station?"

"No, not here. It was a long time ago. I wasn't even making films then. I was working in Atlanta in the spring of 1968 as a researcher for the local public station, my first job after college. My boss called me into his office on the day of Martin Luther King's funeral. The streets were filled with mourners and I could hear the sounds of drums and music. I wanted to be outside. I wanted to be part of it, but I had to work. In television, you're always the observer.

"My boss was very excited. Someone at the station had an idea, a whole night devoted to King's memory, and he wanted me to approach a famous performer who had been an intimate of King and who was in Atlanta for the funeral. 'Offer him anything,' he told me, 'they can sing, they can dance. We don't care what they do. We want his tribute to his friend on our station.' I protested, but he was persistent. 'You can do it, girl. Sell our class, sell our integrity, the superiority of public television over the networks.'

"I was twenty-one, Doug, and I believed him. But I didn't know where to start, how to reach the performer. How could I intrude at a moment like that? But I did. I went to the hotel where he was staying and wrote a letter. Oh, did I write a letter. About a nation's pain, about a nation's need to heal. I sent it to his suite and it worked. He asked me to come up and a sea of faces stared at me when I entered the room. I was the alien, the outsider trying to cash in on their grief. But he seemed to sense my humiliation and perhaps something more: that I was sincere and genuinely believed what I had written in the letter. He was still holding it in his hand when he asked, 'Tell me what you're offering.' I don't know what I said. I remember only that my voice was trembling. He listened. They all listened and then he said he would call me in a few weeks.

"I went back to the station and told my boss what had happened. 'Good going, girl. I knew you could do it,' he said. 'But damn it, I hope he makes up his mind before everybody is up to their ass with tributes to King.'

"The performer called me a few weeks later, just as he said

he would. He was ready to accept our offer and I rushed in to tell my boss. But the words were hardly out of my mouth when he said, 'Christ, I thought I'd told you. We dumped the idea. We can't preempt an entire evening. And we can't give them control. Christ knows what they would say or who they would blame. They might even ask for money. Call him back and tell him the deal is off.'

" 'No,' I said.

" 'Then write him another god-damned letter.'

"I refused and two weeks later, I left the station."

She shivered. He draped his jacket around her shoulders. And as they retraced their steps toward Fifth Avenue, he took her hand. Her first impulse was to withdraw it. She didn't want his sympathy; she didn't need his protection. But he sensed her slight tension and said, "It's okay, Jess. Nothing to worry about. Just two friends holding hands."

"It's the bus for me," she said, when they reached the street. "My expense account days are over."

"Then this ride is on me."

In the cab driving south on Fifth Avenue, both of them were lost in their own thoughts. Jessica remembered the night he had taken her to Columbia University. Central Park, Columbia, it was odd the places they chose to share the pieces of their past. And she recalled that night in the taxi on the way home when they were jostled together and quickly drew apart. They sat closer now, but they did not speak again until they were standing under the awning in front of her building. The doorman nodded at her in recognition and then discreetly turned away, thinking perhaps they wished for a moment alone. Jessica, too, felt a closeness, an intimacy.

"What are you doing the Labor Day weekend?" Doug asked.

"I'll be here, gearing up for job hunting."

"I'll be here, too. Maybe we could have dinner."

"I'd like that."

She realized then that he had no intention of coming any further. He was a friend. She had made him a friend and he would not violate the terms of their truce. Admittedly, she was the one who had kept him at a distance all summer. And she knew he would neither understand nor believe her if she told him that while she had tried, she had not been able to forget him or their night in London. Standing next to him now, there wasn't a part of her that wasn't filled with the memory of his touch, of her head buried in the warm place between his neck and shoulder. But it would only seem that once more she was using him to fill a void, brighten a dark moment, massage a temporarily unhappy heart. He could not forgive her past indifference. And she dared not ask.

Dressing to go out, Jessica was in an all or nothing mood, like the gambler who thrusts his last silver dollar in a slot machine. She wasn't certain what she wanted to win. The jackpot had always been her Thursday nights with Ben. But this wasn't Thursday; Ben had called that morning to say he could get away from the office early. This meeting was unexpected, a new machine with unfamiliar symbols and unknown odds. But she was more than willing to play the game.

They were to meet at the outdoor café in Rockefeller Center, and sitting at a small table waiting for him, surrounded by scores of people at other tables, hundreds more peering over the railing of the promenade above, she felt an unfamiliar and slightly unsettling sensation. It was such a public place, so different from the small dark restaurants where they usually met. But wasn't that a good sign? And when he approached the table and she saw that he was not dressed in the blue-checked shirt and blazer he wore on

Thursdays, but in a rumpled business suit, that was a good sign, too. This was not back street; it was in the open, out of doors. The attaché case he carried was the only reminder of the old rituals, the old context.

"Did you talk to that guy at Channel 8?" he asked, pulling his chair up to the table.

"He took me to lunch. An expensive bottle of wine, but no job. He might have something in the fall."

"How about some free-lance stuff? Just tell me who you want to see and I'll arrange it, Jess."

"I will." She did not say that hustling, selling herself, had always been distasteful. She never told him how nervous she had been at their first meeting five years ago. Equally preposterous would be the admission that the idea of making another film anywhere, for anyone, at this moment held little appeal.

They ordered vodka and tonics. "Paris, Jess," Ben said, raising his glass in a toast. "It's only six weeks away."

When a myth becomes reality, it should provoke more excitement. Instead, Jessica's thoughts were filled with the logistics of the trip. She couldn't afford it, not really, with no job in sight. Could he? In the past when they had been able to get away together, both were on assignment and the station picked up the tab. Would she be an item on his expense account? And would they travel together or separately, register as man and wife or have separate rooms? This was not merely a romantic rendezvous, a lovers' tryst. It was deception on a grand scale. And Ben would have to work during the day while she waited, like a wife, sightseeing, shopping, drifting through churches and museums without him. Alone. When had financial concerns limited her fantasies; when had anticipation become apprehension? But she did not utter any of these thoughts. She said only, "Aren't you forgetting something? I might have a job by then."

He had forgotten. His expression revealed it.

"And there's something else, Ben. If I can't find anything in New York, I'll have to look somewhere else." And this time her thoughts were filled with letters, long-distance phone calls, clandestine meetings in airport hotels. Once a month, once a year?

"God, don't you think I'm worried about that, too, Jess? Ever since you left the station, I've been afraid of losing you."

"Just one day out of your week, Ben. One night."

He looked at her with puzzlement. "Is that all you think you mean to me? You're my life."

"And Sara, your children? What are they?"

"They're different, a different part of me. You've got the best part, Jess. Remember I told you that the first night? You have the part that Sara could never understand, never share."

"And she has a part I've never shared."

A glimmer of comprehension crossed his face. He cupped her hands in his. "That's why I want you to come to Paris. We'll have time to talk. You haven't been yourself, Jess. We can have fun, make plans for the future."

"We've never done that, have we?" she said. "I don't think I can come, Ben."

She withdrew her hands and he saw her drawing away from him. "There's something I was going to tell you in Paris. I was saving it as a surprise. As a matter of fact, it was a surprise to me, too. Sara has offered to give me a divorce."

There was no sense of triumph, no feeling that she had finally secured her goal, planted her banner on a newly claimed territory. A shiver crossed Jessica's shoulders and penetrated her arms to her fingertips.

"Why? Does she know about me?"

"Of course not."

"Did you ask?"

"No," Ben said. "It just came out of the blue one night. Sara has been lonely without the kids. She's been taking courses, wants to get a job and maybe even move to New York. I guess she felt I didn't want her to do that. So she said she would give me a divorce."

Was that all she felt, Jessica wondered? Was that all she had said? And a new vision of Sara began to take shape in her mind. The small fair-haired woman with pale eyes was not the fragile, dependent creature she had pictured in her imagination, a picture Ben had outlined if not actually drawn. She was not a patient in intensive care who would expire without the life support system of her husband, her marriage, but a woman who had just begun to see that she shared only a part of the man she loved—and who could survive without him. Had Ben really understood what Sara meant?

"That is a surprise," she said gravely.

"Then damn it, why aren't you happy? Isn't that what you've been hinting at? Isn't that what all this has been leading up to?"

She couldn't be angry. Her reaction was something close to sorrow. "Is that what you thought? I'm not nineteen. If that's what I wanted, I would have asked."

"Then what do you want?" Ben said in despair. "Just tell me, Jess. I can give it to you."

Even a week ago, the answer to that question would have been easy. But now when she spoke, it was softly, tentatively, expressing feelings she had never put into words before. "I'm not sure I know what I want, Ben. I know I love you. You don't realize how exciting, how intoxicating, it's been, working with you, talking about ideas that mattered, making films that mattered. We were right in the middle of everything. We had the world, we had each other, and when we were together, when you touched me, you brought me to life. I'd do almost anything to keep all that."

"I would, too, Jess. I wish to God you were still at the station."

"But I'm not. And maybe it was too intoxicating, every day spinning madly toward Thursday. It was like a drug that distorts time, distorts perception, and now that it's suddenly been taken away, I feel a little lost. But I can see all the things I never saw before—the little things, the normal things we've never had. Reality. Thursday nights aren't reality. The Ritz isn't reality."

He looked for the waiter, signaled for another round of drinks, and she could sense his discomfort. How many hours had they spent with their heads bowed together over the tables of restaurants while he talked and she listened, absorbing, reflecting, acquiescing to his realities?

"I don't know what to say, Jess. I thought I was offering you everything. What do you want from me?"

"Weekends," she said. "A car ride to the country to see the fall colors. I want to give you a Christmas present you won't have to open at the office and leave there. I want to spend a night with you without making love. And I want you there in the morning when I wake up."

"But it wouldn't be the same, Jess. We wouldn't have what we have now. You'd see my flaws."

"Flaws?"

"You'd hear my early morning creaks, watch me nod off after dinner. It would change things. You would love me less."

His smile was sheepish, his expression boyish, his words uttered in the seductive, self-deprecating style that had amused her for so long. But she looked at him now as she would an acquaintance whose face was disfigured by a birthmark, a blemish she had never noticed before.

"Don't you think I've seen your flaws?" she said. "Don't you think I've felt your fatigue? Am I so perfect that I require you to be perfect? What kind of love would that be?"

"The kind of love I need. I'm older than you, Jess. And you make time stand still."

"But I'm not a magic elixir, a fountain of youth . . ."

"You are for me. And I want to stay the same for you. I never want you to be disappointed in me."

He stroked her hand and she recognized the gesture, provocative, sensual. He was, of course, thinking about sex, not arthritic morning hands or dozing after dinner. And he was talking about it as if she were voracious, insatiable, demanding perpetual youth, a perpetual erection. Was it her fault? Had she nourished this cockeyed fantasy? By compressing and confining their moments together, had they sexualized their intimacy, stunted their love? "And our ideas, our feelings and everything else we shared? You have no faith they would endure either?"

"Of course they will. I just don't want you to see me grow old."

Another dose of protection. She tried to speak, to protest, but it was impossible to put her thoughts into words. She had believed that their love was narrowed only by the dimension of time. Now she saw that it was distorted by his perception of her. He saw her as a different species of woman from his wife. Sara was strong enough to observe the immutable acts of growing older and love him still. Sara's love could endure disappointment. It was she, not Sara, who was the fragile hothouse flower that must be sheltered from change. And with that realization she felt depleted, diminished, as if a giant syringe had penetrated an artery, draining her body of blood.

"I can't help it, Jess," he said. "That's how I love you."

"But I don't understand what you think I love about you."

"Beats the hell out of me, too," he said laughing.

A breeze swirled around them, rippling the yellow awnings of the café. The flags lining the promenade flapped noisily, but Jessica heard another sound—the sound of a vase smashing against a wall, roses spilling everywhere. At last she did understand. And exhausted by her own tenacity, she finally admitted to herself that she was engaged in a battle she couldn't and didn't want to win. He was a juggler terrified of dropping any one of the many balls he tried to keep in the air. He would never leave the station, no matter what compromises he was forced to make. He was happy there. And he would never leave Sara. He was happy there, too. They were his life support system, and he would never need anything more from her than an occasional reassurance that he was ageless, flawless, perfect. She did not hate him for that. She just didn't love him any more.

"Let's go back to your apartment, Jess," he said. "Before dinner, like we used to."

"No," she said, shaking her head solemnly.

"It's what happened at the station, isn't it? Your film, your job. I did what I could."

"I'm not blaming you for that, Ben."

"You'll get another job. We'll have what we've always had. We'll have more. I promise."

"That's impossible. I know that now."

She started to rise, but he took her hand and pulled her back. "I won't let you do this. I won't let you throw away four years."

"I'm not throwing them away. I'll remember them forever."

"No one will ever love you the way I do."

"Ben, please let go of my hand. Let me go. It isn't the end of the world, yours or mine. Only one small part of it."

She got up, holding her hand to her hair to protect it from the wind. She was smiling but behind the smile she felt as if she had just uncurled her fingers from the edge of a cliff and was falling, falling through an empty and eternal space.

He looked up at her, his eyes pleading. "Can I call you? Can I see you?"

"Of course, Ben. In time."

She kissed him lightly on the forehead, then left the café and ran quickly up the steep flight of steps that led to the promenade. When she reached the top and knew he couldn't see her, she turned her head to look at him for a moment. He was sitting exactly where she had left him. He had not moved.

TWENTY-ONE

*T*he camera she had used on others to distance and sharpen, seduce and disarm, was still focused on her own life. And in close-up or longshot, no matter how she tried to rework the memory, her parting from Ben seemed a pale climax, a slow dissolve, instead of a finale with fireworks and an abrupt fadeout. He called every day to say he loved her, his conversations wavering between simple hellos and requests to see her—a drink, lunch, dinner. It didn't matter. And each time she refused him gently, disguising the pain she felt when she heard the urgency in his voice.

She had lost so much—essential parts of her, as if her

work and her love for Ben had been her eyes, her hands, her heart. Without premeditation, in two impulsive acts, she had torn the fabric of her life to shreds. She had confronted Lyman, she had confronted Ben, and walked away not in victory, but into a void. Yet as part of her grieved, another part observed her grief. Her sadness gave way to an examination of the nature of her sadness. And the reasons for her loss remained unresolved.

She felt the tug of another loss when she looked at the bookcase and saw a print of her film. Jeff had a copy made in the lab and sent it by messenger, scribbling, "Write when you get work," on the card tucked inside the can. Work? There wasn't an opening for a documentary filmmaker in all of New York, or so it seemed. And as she sifted through the possibilities, it was apparent that she was, after more than ten years in television, as ill prepared for any other kind of work as she was for the idleness she had been unable to transform into leisure. Still she tried to be optimistic. After all, Max, struggling to produce a prickly new bud, had somehow managed to make the adjustment from the darkness of a desk drawer to the bright light of her window sill. Perhaps after three days of solitude over the Labor Day weekend, she, too, would emerge, ready to face a new season. Labor Day had always been her New Year's Eve, fall her spring, her time of beginnings. But she couldn't rid herself of the feeling that, after impetuously abandoning ship, she was adrift at sea without any notion of which direction to take to make it safely back to shore.

Wanda was the first to throw her a line. She called with an invitation. "Mel is driving me absolutely up the wall and I'm coming into the city on Friday just to restore my sanity. Have lunch with me and then spend the weekend with us at the beach."

Jessica begged off. "I planned on staying here. I have to sort out my life."

"Sort out your life?" Wanda pounced on the words like a cat. "Mel is dying to see you. And I need your help closing up the house. Then you can sort out your life. I won't take no for an answer. Meet me at the apartment and we'll leave early to beat the traffic."

Kate also had an invitation. "Can you come to dinner on Sunday? Paul is flying in from London and we both want to see you. I promise I won't cook. I thought we might try one of the new soul food restaurants in our neighborhood."

"I'd love to," Jessica said, "but I'm spending the weekend with Mel and Wanda Shane in Montauk. Let's make a date for next week. I've got a lot to tell you."

"Good news or bad?"

"I've broken up with Ben."

"I see." Obviously Kate was not surprised. "How do you feel?"

"Not terrific, not terrible," Jessica replied. "The tides are very still. I'll call you when I get back to the city. And give my love to Paul."

A young man with curly hair and a moustache opened the door to the Shanes' apartment, and when Jessica heard Wanda's voice calling her from the bedroom, she thought perhaps she had arrived too early. Who knew what Wanda might need to restore her sanity?

She was lying on a massage table, her body draped in a sheet, her head wrapped in a terrycloth towel. "This muscular little creature is Mario," she said. "Mario, Jessica. He'll be finished in ten minutes, but it's too gruesome to watch. Lunch is all ready. Just mix the salad and make yourself a drink."

Grinning broadly, Mario began pouring oil on Wanda's

feet. "I've told you a hundred times, darling," she said, "my toes are fine. Perfect. Thighs, Mario, thighs."

From the moment they entered the car and began their crawl through the congested streets of the city, Wanda pumped Jessica about everything. "Well, you don't look like a woman who just told Lyman Ellis to go to hell and walked out of her job. A little pale, perhaps. Some salt air and sunshine will do you good."

"Do I look like a woman who's just walked out on the man she's loved for four years?"

Wanda was unruffled. "Sometimes that can be a very healthy experience. Who was he, your boss? And married, of course."

"How did you know?"

"I've been there, darling. It gives a woman a certain look —as long as it lasts. What happened, did he go back to his wife?"

"He never left her. And I don't think he ever will. But it wasn't that. He loved me, he still does, but I know now what kind of love it was, what kind of need. Anyway, it's over."

"Four years is a long time," Wanda said, her eyes fixed on the traffic streaming all around them. "I was married for less time than that to a man I didn't love at all, and even that wasn't an easy ending. But don't hate him, darling. Hold on to the best parts. It's always wise to treat a broken love affair like a lousy fruitcake. Forget the figs, the dates, the raisins, and just remember the taste of the rum."

With only an occasional curse, Wanda maneuvered the car skillfully along crowded highways and convoluted interchanges until, finally, broad ribbons of concrete narrowed to winding roads bordered by sandy ditches and scrub pine. A clean salt smell permeated the air, but the sun had disappeared and dark angry clouds rolled across the sky by the time she turned into a rutted driveway that led to a large

A-frame house sitting high on a dune. "I don't like the looks of that sky," she said, glancing quickly at herself in the rearview mirror. "But we're here. This is it. Mel calls it Casa Albatross."

He was standing at the head of the long flight of steps that climbed to the back deck of the house. When Jessica reached the top, she dropped her bag and embraced him. "You don't look at all surprised to see me."

"Not for a second. I knew Wanda would make you an offer you couldn't refuse." He reached for Jessica's bag, but Wanda snatched it from his hands. "You see how she treats me," he muttered. "I enjoyed it for a while, but between total sobriety and a wife playing Mother Earth, I'm slowly dying of boredom. My life expectancy was better when she was indifferent."

Beneath a tall cathedral ceiling, the long living room of the house swept toward a wall of windows framing a steel gray sky indistinguishable from the color of the sea. Just as Wanda's New York apartment was quintessentially Park Avenue, so this was basic beach house: white wicker furniture, jute mats, and an explosion of upholstery and pillows as brightly colored as a tropical bird. She decorated everything, including herself, as if she were in a competition to define the true nature of things. And she had performed an equally expert job on her husband. Mel was transformed. Gone the pasty pallor that had marked his complexion for months, gone the paunch that had bulged over his belt buckle. His face was the color of butterscotch, his big body firm. Only his straggly red hair was the same. Everything else was contained.

"You look wonderful," Jessica said.

"You don't look so bad yourself considering all that's happened. But we'll talk about that later. Come on, I want to show you my ocean."

They stepped out on the front deck where another long flight of stairs, almost buried in sand and dunegrass, descended to the broad beach. A fine rain borne by the rising wind stung their faces, the surf crashed over the beach with a continuous roar. "Pretty impressive, isn't it?" Mel said in the proprietary tone of a man who owns a fine piece of the planet.

"It suits my mood," Jessica replied.

Wanda refused her help in the kitchen. "Nothing elaborate tonight, darling. We're eating white. Remember?"

Jessica remembered. Half in jest, she had once confessed to Wanda that she was convinced the color of food had a profound psychological effect, and the ingestion of white food was a sure cure for dark moments of the soul. "I know it's probably a wish to regress to some infantile state," she had explained. "Farina, milk, a cocoon of mashed potatoes. But once in a while, regression is a necessary prelude to change."

Mel was tending the fire he had built in the modern black metal stove in the living room. "Would you believe she can cook, too?" he said with a shrug. "What the hell am I going to do with her, Jess? When I married her—what was it, two, three years ago—I thought to myself, why not? Another beautiful broad, another notch on my gun. You only live once. She'll stick around like the others for a while, then get fed up and take me for every penny I'm worth. But it isn't working out that way and now I'm stuck with her. Mean, ruthless. You should hear the way she talks to me sometimes, the way she talks to my kids. She's as crafty and fierce as a lioness protecting her cubs. And so help me God, I love every minute of it."

He attacked the fire with a poker, sending a shower of sparks into the room, and Jessica realized that all the old impatience, his interfering, domineering ways, his angry determination to right the world's wrongs, were still there. Wanda hadn't changed that. She had merely given him a healthy dose of his own medicine.

"But we didn't drag you all the way out here to talk about the life and love of Mel and Wanda Shane," he said. "Doug has kept me posted, and it's a damned shame, Jess. But frankly, I'm surprised you didn't quit a long time ago. Lyman Ellis is an unprincipled, two-faced son of a bitch."

If Mel and Wanda had invited her with some thought of soothing her troubles, Jessica knew now that the last thing she could expect from either of them was sympathy. "You're right, of course. People leave their jobs all the time."

Wanda was setting the table behind them. "But people rarely lose a job and a lover all in the same century. It seems our Jessica made a fundamental mistake, darling. She fell for the boss and she's left him, too. Dinner's ready. Can I trust you to open the wine?"

As they took their places at the table, Mel studied Jessica with an expression of puzzlement. But he said nothing while Wanda served them heaping plates of linguine and white clam sauce sprinkled with powdery Parmesan cheese. "Your boss?" Mel said finally, pouring the wine. "Boy, am I the prize sap. And all these years I've been trying to fix you up with every available male that crossed my path."

"Sometimes availability is not an asset," Wanda remarked.

"I'm an interfering old bastard and I'm sorry," Mel said. "I'm the one who got you into this mess, urging Doug on you . . ."

"Doug had nothing to do with it," Jessica said, almost too quickly.

"He had everything to do with the case against the drug. I urged that on you, too."

"I had to beg Doug to let me make that film."

"But if it weren't for me and my meddling . . ."

"Mel, stop it," Jessica said. "If anyone is responsible, I am. I had a job and I made it a calling. I had an affair, a liaison, and I made it something else. Don't feel sorry for me."

"I don't," Wanda said in her solemn, knowing way. "It's your boss I feel sorry for. It's always harder for the one who has to stay."

The salad was raw cauliflower, which Mel regarded with disgust, and for dessert, a runny white cheese served with Italian bread, the jarring brown crust removed. They had coffee in front of the fire. "Doug says you made a great film," Mel said. "Any chance it'll ever be shown?"

"No, none."

"Well, don't worry about it. We'll get them, Jess, the whole dirty lot. My sentence is almost over. I'll be back in the city next week . . ."

"So will I," Wanda snapped. "And if you think I'm going to let you kill yourself all over again . . ."

"For Christ's sake, Wanda," Mel shouted. "This is important."

"I know, darling. I know," she said sadly. "I'll have that engraved on your tombstone. Come on, you've had enough excitement for one day. It's time for bed."

"Did you hear that, Jess? Bed is where we go now when we've had too much excitement. Alas, we are getting old."

Jessica sat alone in front of the stove, watching the orange flames dance and then slowly die. Her thoughts were of Ben and she couldn't help wondering, as she had wondered for four years of weekends, what he was doing now, where he was. Did he have a fireplace? And was he sitting with Sara, staring into the flames, thinking of her? She had always imagined that it would take a painful act of will to force her to forget him. But now she found she did not have to forget.

Her questions were merely a reflex, for her memories of him were not searing flames, but the warm glowing ashes of a fire that has consumed its fuel.

She went to the windows overlooking the beach. The wind howling around the corners of the house sounded like the shriek of a thousand tea kettles; rain pelted against the glass and the surf resonated like a continuous clap of thunder. Standing there, she felt the anger of the ocean. But how could she rail at the gods? How could she complain or feel even an ounce of self-pity? Because the ocean demands the truth, she was forced to admit there was no one to blame for what had happened but herself. Just as she had mistaken the nature of Ben's love, his need for her, so she had failed to understand the nature of her own need. Yet she could not lament the loss of the part of her that believed she had no existence without him. And with that revelation she recognized another truth: her need to love, not merely to be loved, whatever the odds, whatever the dangers.

Flushed with the excitement that came from confronting these fresh realities, she wanted to leave the house, walk along the beach, test herself against the storm. She tugged at the sliding glass door, but it was jammed with wet sand. She could not see the ocean. The glass, transformed into a mirror by the blackness of the night, reflected her own image, and she felt like a woman who has put on her makeup, donned a new dress, only to discover she has no place to go.

It was a perfect September morning. The blue of the sky streaked with filmy white clouds matched the color of the sea, making an almost seamless connection. The storm had cleared the air, swept the beach clean, and the day promised to be as crisp and bright as cellophane. Wanda and Mel were seated at the table when Jessica descended the narrow circular staircase that led from her loft bedroom to the rooms below. In fact, they had already jogged the prescribed distance along the beach and this was their second breakfast, not the panoply of white food Jessica expected, oatmeal and soft-boiled eggs, but bowls of fresh fruit, raisins, nuts, and toasted grains.

"We've entered a new phase," Mel announced, carefully peeling a banana. "Monkey food. I hope you can do better for dinner, Wanda, or Doug will think this is a zoo."

"Doug is coming?" Jessica asked, aware that Wanda was studying her reaction.

"Oh, didn't I tell you? He accepted at the last minute. Funny, it must have slipped my mind."

"Does he know I'll be here?"

"I may have mentioned it," was Wanda's terse reply.

After breakfast, Jessica went for a walk along the beach, letting the sun draw the chill from her body—the chill of the editing room, the shivers of coldness she had felt filming Timmy Harcent, the icy despair that had gripped her the afternoon Ben said, "You'd see my flaws. . . . You would love me less." And for the first time in months, she felt warm, light, expectant, without knowing the reason why. She inspected the irridescent shells washed ashore by the storm, waded in the swirling pools left behind by the receding tide, and sitting on a small ledge of sand sculptured by the pounding waves, watched the sandpipers play their timeless game with the sea. Scurrying along the foamy water's edge, they darted bravely forward, then retreated to safety with the sweep of every breaking wave. Was it courage or merely instinct, Jessica wondered? What would happen if they miscalculated, took a foolish risk, dared come too close, if once the waves were victorious? Would they merely get wet, or drown?

Doug arrived toward the middle of the afternoon and

from his greeting she couldn't tell if he was surprised to see her. Or pleased. It had crossed her mind that Bambi might be with him. But he was alone and, it seemed to Jessica, in a gray mood inappropriate to the day. Sitting on the deck facing the sea, their talk was of summer's ending, of Mel's ruddy good health, and Jessica recounted what was becoming the standard version of her confrontation with Lyman Ellis, embellishing it with humorous exaggerations of his villainy and her own naive heroism.

Doug was not amused. "It's not funny, Jess," he said, glowering at her. "Now we've both lost."

"What have *you* lost?" she asked sarcastically.

"The case, damn it! McCampbell's lawyers pulled some arcane statute out of their hats and the Court of Appeals refused to uphold the injunction. McCampbell can start selling their goddamned drug."

"That's impossible," Jessica cried.

"Probably," Doug said. "No thanks to me. But the news isn't all bad. There was a ruling yesterday against Styralon in the English courts. The Harcents were awarded four hundred thousand pounds. And a few hours after the judgment was announced, the Committee on the Safety of Medicines pulled the drug off the market. The FDA *has* to take action now."

"Doug, congratulations." Jessica reached out and shook his hand.

"That's okay," Mel said, "but not terrific. I thought you were going to nail those bastards with a criminal indictment."

"That's up to the federal attorneys. They have all the evidence, including a transcript of your film, Jess. If they think they've got a case, they'll take it before a grand jury. It's out of my hands. And I feel so damn helpless."

"I know," Jessica said. "I felt the same way about my film.

It's sad, isn't it? My film will never be shown and you'll never have a chance to argue the case. Somehow, we've both been cheated."

"Cheated?" Mel exploded. "What the hell's the matter with you two? You're going to win. You should be jubilant. That damned drug will never be sold in this country, I'll bet on it, and you did it. It was *because* of the film, the threat of it, *because* of the case, the *fact* of it, that all this is happening. So you won't make headlines, you won't get the glory. Okay, it's tough to work as hard as you did and then have your soapboxes stolen out from under you. I like a little applause myself from time to time."

"I'll try to remember that," Wanda said. "Now calm down, darling."

"I am calm. All I'm saying is it's easy to work for applause. But sometimes we all have to settle for silent praise and maybe, if we're lucky, a little gratitude some day. If you expect more than that, you're both in the wrong business."

The two men walked along the beach, Doug with bare feet and his pants legs rolled. Mel was carrying a seabass wrapped in newspaper, purchased from one of the seiners along the shore who was casting his net into the sea and scooping up his catch with ease. "It does lack a certain amount of justice and fair play, I'll have to admit," Mel remarked.

"No, you were right," Doug said. "Stopping the damn drug is what we were after. Screw the recognition."

"Who's talking about you?" Mel said. "I'm talking about the fish. No lines, no bait, no sport. This poor bastard never had a chance."

"I can't get emotionally involved with a fish."

Mel saw his opening and took it. "You can't get emotionally involved with anyone," he said sourly.

"And what the hell does that mean?"

"Forget it. I was just thinking about Jessica. She gets involved. So he was married. At least it was a step in the right direction. I suppose you didn't know about that?"

"As a matter of fact, I did."

Mel was clearly disappointed, hoping to shock Doug as he had been shocked. "Well, it's over. She's walked out on him. I suppose you knew that, too?"

"No, that I didn't know."

"So what are you going to do about it?"

Doug looked at him with exasperation. "Nothing, Mel. And will you please stay out of my life? It just so happens I once knew a woman like Jessica and I'm no longer attracted to the type."

"So you made your move and she shot you down, right? Big deal. It happens all the time. I had to chase Wanda for months before she'd even look at me. You can spend the rest of your life sleeping with airheads if that's what you really want. It's all the same to me. But what the hell's the matter with Jessica?"

Doug was too familiar with Mel's intrusions to be annoyed. "All right, if you want to know the truth, she's as cold as that fish." But even as he spoke, he knew that wasn't the truth. "I can't explain it, Mel. It's just that she always seems to be somewhere else. Out of reach." Yet that wasn't the truth either, for he remembered the time in London when all of her had been there.

"But did you ever ask yourself why? What she's afraid of? And what the hell are *you* afraid of?"

"Lay off, Mel," Doug said. "And for your information, my friend, you make a lousy Cupid."

They returned to the house where Mel displayed the fish to Wanda as proudly as if he had caught it himself. "Look, darling, isn't he grand?"

She made a face, screwed up and sour. "You don't expect me to clean that, do you?"

"Don't worry," he said, spreading newspapers over the table on the front deck. "I'll take care of the fish. Where's Jess?"

"Down on the beach," Wanda replied, "sorting out her life."

"Did you bring your suit?" Mel asked Doug. "Why don't you go for a swim?"

"I have a little chore for him right here," Wanda said, pointing at a bucket of oysters. Even in a bathing suit, a basket of corn between her legs, Wanda was relentlessly chic, a weird combination of city slickery and child of nature. Her skin was the color of honey, her makeup faultless, every hair in place. She was the beach personified, but clearly a stranger to the sea.

"Do you want the head on or off?" Mel asked.

"Off, darling, please. I don't like food that looks at me."

"And what am I supposed to do with these?" Doug said, inspecting the oysters with apprehension.

"Open them, of course."

So they sat, Wanda shucking corn, Mel scraping the scales of a seabass and Doug poking at the shell of an oyster with a knife. Refugees from a world where people were paid to do things like that, they all felt a little silly performing such unnatural natural acts.

"Damn," Doug grumbled, sucking the finger he had just jabbed with the knife. "I can't seem to get the hang of this."

"Persistence, darling," Wanda said, ripping husks from the corn with scarlet-tipped fingers. "There's one tiny little soft spot, and if you can find that, the rest is easy. Like love."

"Easy," Mel said. "You can look at this battle-scarred old body and say love is easy?"

"I'm not talking about marriage, darling. That's hard work."

"And once-in-a-while love?" Mel asked, decapitating the fish and tossing the head over the railing onto the dunes. "What's that?"

"That," Wanda said, "is like taking one little pill and hoping you can make the feeling last. Sometimes it works, but it's usually the wrong prescription." She examined a wormy ear of corn and tossed it aside with a frown.

"So now you're saying love is like a drug?" Mel remarked. "As if we need it, like junkies, just for the effect."

"That's right, darling. You're the aphrodisiac of my spirit, and that ain't bad."

Doug knew this conversation was designed for his benefit. Wanda was much more oblique than Mel, if no less intrusive. "I want a woman to want me for me, not for the way I make her feel," Doug said, struggling with what seemed like a permanently closed oyster that would not yield to his knife.

"Then that should work both ways, shouldn't it?" Wanda said sweetly, turning her attention to a bag of string beans that she began to snap expertly. "But I'm not talking about just sex, you know. There are wonderful side effects, too. Love is the way you feel before—and after. Love is the way you feel when sex is the furthest thing from your mind. It's talking and not having to talk. It's needing and being needed . . ."

"In short, pure hell," Mel said. He and Doug exchanged glances, condescending, as mysterious as smoke signals, as old as mankind.

"That's right, darling," Wanda said. "And don't look so smug. I know there's an enormous difference between men and women, a chasm we both have to cross. And it's a

terrible risk. There's only one thing you can be absolutely sure of, and that's the fact of love, that it exists, that it's out there somewhere, no matter how tough it is to find or how tough to keep."

"A minute ago you said love was easy," Doug remarked. "And now you say it's tough. Make up your mind, Wanda."

"You weren't listening. I said it was like opening an oyster. You have to know the secret."

Wanda leaned over the table to look at Mel's fish, which he had arranged in narrow, white fillets for her inspection. "Beautiful, darling." Her reaction was less complimentary when she examined Doug's progress with the oysters. "Next time I'll buy them in one of those little cardboard containers. But then that wouldn't be much of a challenge, would it?"

She and Mel gathered up their contributions to the dinner table and left Doug alone on the deck, still baffled by the oysters. Jessica would not be pleased, he thought, to hear Wanda compare her to an oyster. She was a challenge, damn it. But his struggle was not only with her. It was with himself. He had wanted to do much more than hold her hand that afternoon in Central Park. And as he stood under the awning in front of her building, he had to battle the impulse to take her in his arms, ask if he could come up to her apartment. Had he seen an invitation in her eyes? He wasn't sure. He was sure only of the way she had made him feel that night in London, all the parts of him, mind and body together, a coalition that had happened only once before. But again those feelings had betrayed him, and now he remembered the weeks of indifference and isolation she had caused him to endure. The knowledge that she was taken, had a lover, was no consolation. He could have faced that kind of competition if he had been certain he wanted to win the game. He had finally met a woman with whom he might

be able to share everything. And it was a grim, baleful irony that she was a woman who had been content with only the spare pieces and parts of a married man.

Now that he knew her love affair was over, his situation seemed even more difficult. For if he approached her again, she would accuse him once more of taking unfair advantage, of being attracted only by her vulnerability. But that was not the reason he was still drawn to her. He was intrigued by the strength that masked that vulnerability, the cynicism and cunning that concealed her naivete. Stirred by her intellectual passion, challenged by her independence, moved by the intense idealism that could lead to such dark despair. He had seen it all, watching her make the film; and in the film itself, her many contradictions had come together. She wasn't in it, yet she was there. And now she was here.

He looked up to see her walking toward the house from the beach. Dressed in a bathing suit, her hair in damp curls clinging to her head, she moved closer with each step, a silhouette against the sand. Her bare shoulders and arms, her long legs, were a soft white, untouched by the summer sun, and he remembered that her body, like her spirit, could be both taut and tender. If he wanted to experience that sensation again, why was he, so combative in a courtroom, meekly, docilely abiding by her rules? Why wasn't he battling harder for her, for himself?

Wanda permitted Jessica into the kitchen to finish the preparations for their meal. At her touch, Doug's oysters were transformed into a creamy stew, Mel's seabass was brushed with lemon juice and butter and put in the oven to bake, the beans, cooked briefly and then chilled in a vinaigrette, became the salad. Only the corn, fresh that day from nearby fields, would be boiled and served without embellishment. "All these calories," she said. "But what the hell. Mel has been such a good sport and this is a special occasion."

"What were you three talking about on the deck?" Jessica asked. "Doug gave me the most peculiar look when I came back to the house."

"I was just shooting my mouth off as usual," Wanda said. "I don't know why I bother. Men are completely hopeless. How long have you been in love with Doug?"

"We're just friends, Wanda. Nothing more."

"If you say so. But I'll tell you something about your 'friend.' I never used to like him very much. He was too cocky, too self-satisfied. And you, my sweet, with your serene smile, I thought you had all the makings of a closet bitch."

"I wasn't mad about you, either."

"I know. Just another one of Mel's overdressed and undersexed acquisitions. We all give lousy first impressions. But people change. And so do their perceptions of other people."

"And you think Doug has changed?"

"Enormously. It's taken a while, but he's finally figured out what Mel is all about."

"And me?"

Stooping at the stove, Wanda basted the fish. "That depends on how long it takes you to pick yourself up and move on. You could do worse than Doug. I've seen the way you've been looking at him, too."

"Oh, Wanda, I don't know. I think he has me marked as the woman who seduced him and ran."

"You did that, did you?" Wanda said, pushing her glasses up on her nose and peering at Jessica with renewed interest. "And how did he make you feel?"

"Scared."

"Perfect."

"I guess that's why I ran."

"Well, slow down, my sweet. Give the man a chance to catch up with you. He's scared, too, you know. Men are always frightened when they think they have to give up some ancient right. And women are terrified of assuming anything new. But that's where it all begins."

"How can I, Wanda? Look at me, look at my life. I can't flutter after him like a wounded bird."

"Better wounded than caged, darling. And what makes you think his life is so perfect? He's still testing his wings, too. We all bargain from weakness. Otherwise bargains wouldn't be necessary." Wanda lifted the lid from the pot of corn, the steam from the boiling water fogging her glasses. "This is done. Hand me that bowl, will you? I can't see a thing."

The fish came out of the oven, the beans out of the refrigerator, and Wanda arranged them on a large white stoneware platter, with wedges of lemon and sprigs of parsley. "Let's get this food on the table," she said. "If I know Mel, he's out there giving your friend the benefit of his own peculiar wisdom. And that could ruin everything."

"You're incorrigible," Jessica said. "Both of you. How did you ever get together?"

"Like two locomotives speeding in opposite directions on the same track. The poor guy never knew what hit him. We had no idea what we were getting into. And we're still picking through the wreckage. That's not your style, I know. But you can proceed with caution and never reach your destination. And that, my sweet, is my last word on the subject of love."

It was the sort of evening that did not evoke spirited conversation, the end of a season, and only Mel, with his boundless optimism, looked forward to cutting the ribbon of a new season with any eagerness. Doug, still stung by his defeat in court, listened with only mild interest to Mel's descriptions of the new cases, the new causes, that lay before them. Wanda brooded about the problem she was going to have in striking a healthy balance between her husband's heart and his head. And Jessica was drawn to the memory of her film and the realization that it had been as much about love as about money and power. Like the flickering pictures of the Moviola, visions of Laurel Harcent and Bertha Bowen flashed before her eyes, just as they had the night she visited Mel in the hospital after his attack. These were women for whom love meant survival. And now other women joined that montage of faces: Madge Barwick and the kind of toxic love that destroyed, Sara Nevins, only a shadow on the screen, but with enough substance to exist without Ben's love. But dominating them all, Wanda Shane, wielding her love like a sword. Where did the kind of love she had felt for Ben fit in, Jessica wondered? Where the kind of love she knew she had begun to feel for Doug?

"Best damn meal I've had in months," Mel said, leaning back in his chair with a contented sigh. "There's nothing you can't do, Wanda, when you put your mind to it."

"Are you just discovering that?" she replied.

They had moved to chairs around the fire when the phone rang, jarring them all from the intimacy of the moment. "Damn," Wanda said. "Who would call at this hour?" She picked it up. "It's for you, Jessica," she said with a frown. "A man."

Jessica felt a tingle of apprehension. Had Ben found out where she was, and why was he calling her here? As she went to the phone, she sensed Doug staring at her with X-ray eyes that seemed to penetrate her very core.

"Hello. No, of course not. How did you find me?" Then

for several minutes Jessica was silent, listening, until finally she exclaimed with excitement, "I don't believe it. Are they serious? On Tuesday. I'll be there. How can I thank you? I love you, too."

Returning to the circle of chairs around the fire, Jessica saw that everyone was looking at her now with curious expressions. "I think I may have a job," she said.

"That was your former boss, I suppose," Wanda said with ill-disguised acrimony.

"No, a friend. Paul Marchand. I told his wife I would be here. You remember him, Doug. He's the one who helped us find Daniel Bowen. He's just come from London and says Styralon is front-page news over there. It seems a British station wants to talk to me about making a film for them."

"What about the film you made here?" Doug asked.

"This would be different. Not just about the drug, but all of it. Paul told them what happened to my film and that would be part of the story: how the drug got as far as it did, the TML connection, and why my film hasn't been shown. It's too good to be true. Eight weeks, all expenses paid."

Mel's smile was of the seven-letter variety. "That's terrific, sweetheart. Maybe there's a little justice in the world after all."

Doug, staring into the fire, said nothing.

It was Mel, not Wanda, with noisy yawns and an elaborate show of fatigue, who suggested it was time they went to bed. They left Doug and Jessica sitting in front of the fire. "So it's back to London for you?" he said, tossing another log into the mouth of the stove. Back to where he had first discovered her, he thought. And then lost her.

"I want to go," Jessica said. "It would be the kind of film I've always dreamed of making, one giant film about everything."

"And sweet revenge."

"That, too. But I'm not sure. If I get the job, it might mean permanent exile. Lyman Ellis could see to it that I never work in television again."

"To hell with Lyman Ellis! You can't play it safe, not now, Jess. If you do this film, the case will be closed on Styralon forever. And I'll never have to set foot inside a courtroom."

"That bothers me, too," she said. "It was your case, your story. It doesn't seem fair." She moved her chair closer to the fire, closer to him. "Do you think I should go?"

"You're damn right I do."

She was torn. Part of her wanted his blessing for the trip, but another part wanted him to ask her to stay. It felt as if he was sending her away, back to a world he held in contempt, where the camera abstracted reality and time was measured in microseconds. Perhaps he believed she couldn't change. Perhaps he hadn't changed at all.

"Let me rephrase that," Doug said. "I want you to go if that's what you want." He got up and walked away from the fire. "Come on, let's take a look at the ocean."

They found sweaters, pulled them on, and stepped out on the deck. A sliver of moon illuminated the beach and etched a sparkling path far out to sea. They took off their shoes and walked toward the quietly breaking waves.

"Do you remember London?" she asked tentatively.

"Of course I remember. I thought you were the one who had forgotten."

"I tried but I couldn't. I remember everything. The vase of roses I threw at the wall, the white curtains fluttering at the windows, the way you made me feel."

"You could have fooled me," he said in a voice little more than a whisper.

This was difficult for her, and clearly he did not intend to make it any easier. "There were reasons," she began softly. "Things I couldn't tell you. I had to run."

"I know all about it."

"Know what?"

"Your phantom Thursday night lover."

She had been speaking to the ocean, her words almost lost in the sound of the surf. But now she faced him in anger. "He was much more than that, Doug. Much more. And Bambi? What was she to you?"

"Much less," he said simply.

Jessica shook her fist in the direction of the house. "Damn Wanda. Damn Mel. They told you, didn't they?"

"A lawyer never reveals his sources," he said. "How long will you mourn, Jess?"

"I don't know." Her eyes followed the silver streak of moonlight on the sea.

"I'll give you until Thanksgiving."

Before she understood the meaning of his words, he placed his hands on her cheeks and brought her face close to his. The wash of a breaking wave curled around their bare feet. "Now say it again. Tell me how difficult, how goddamned impossible it was to forget me."

She struggled to get away from him, but he refused to let her go. "Yes, yes, it was impossible . . ."

"Say it again. Tell me it was impossible."

"*You're* impossible," she cried, then broke into laughter at the absurdity of his forcing this confession from her again and again as some sort of penance.

"How can you laugh at a time like this? Can't you keep a straight face even in a love scene?"

"Is that what this is?" she said, twisting away from him.

They walked along the beach, flirting with the waves like sandpipers. "I've got a confession to make, too," he said. "I couldn't forget you either. But every time I tried to come close, you ran."

"I know. But I'm not running now."

Their arms were around each other's waists as they found their way back to the house. Tiptoeing across the living room, carrying his shoes, Doug whispered, "I think we ought to wake up Mel and Wanda. It's all been a giant conspiracy, you know. Shouldn't we tell them their efforts have finally paid off?"

"Don't you dare," Jessica said, her hand on the railing of the staircase that led up to her room. "Where are you supposed to sleep?"

"Mel showed me how to open the couch. But who said anything about sleep? Your place or mine?"

"Mine," she said.

"Okay. You'll have a tough time getting away from me up there."

"But you have to promise me something. Promise you'll make time last."

Mel and Wanda did not have to be told. But there were no smirks or smiles of triumph from Mel, no words of wisdom from Wanda when Jessica and Doug appeared for breakfast. That mission accomplished, they had other matters on their minds. They had decided to return to the city on Sunday to avoid the crush of Labor Day traffic, and Wanda supervised the morning's activities like a drill sergeant. Jessica helped her strip beds and pack, Doug loaded the car, while Mel, relegated to idleness, shouted instructions that Wanda usually ignored. "I hate closing up a house," she said to Jessica as they were finishing the last of their chores. "It's like a divorce. We have a handyman who puts up the shutters and drains the pipes before things get nasty. Mel's kids sometimes come out in the fall. Maybe you and Doug would like to use it?"

"I hope I'll be in England," Jessica said.

"Then you'll take the job?"

"Yes. But I would be back by Thanksgiving."

"Thank God the summer is over," Mel said to Doug. "I've never felt so useless in my life."

"When are you going to learn a little patience?" Doug said. "You'd be surprised at what you can accomplish."

Finally everything was done and they went for one last walk on the beach to bid a ritual farewell to the summer and the sea. The air was cool and there were only a few people in the water or lying on the sand. Others were folding up beach chairs, shaking blankets and towels, gathering up hampers and toys.

"I'm not good at separations, Jess," Doug said.

"And I've never been very good at proximity," she replied.

"I don't care where you are or what you're doing. Make films halfway around the world. Win awards. Just don't become inaccessible."

"It's a long shot, Doug. The odds may be against us."

"What do you think they are?"

"Better."

"Better than what?"

"Better than yesterday."

Jessica saw a man wrestling to close a large red-and-white-striped beach umbrella and that familiar half smile came to her face, borne this time not from a secret sense of security but from the realization that her life would no longer be safe. She had left the magic circle, the white light of Ben's love and protection, and her course seemed as unpredictable as the sea. There would be moments of calm, moments of tumultuous motion, but never would she be the still, tideless body of water she had always feared. Her future as a filmmaker was uncertain, her future with Doug a mystery yet to unfold. Risks and dangers everywhere, darkness, and in sharp contrast, the brilliant colors of unreflected light. But she saw them now through the prism of her own eyes.

Mel and Wanda, so close there was hardly a sliver of space between them, marched slowly back to the house. Jessica and Doug lingered at the water's edge to watch the sandpipers, teasing, taunting a breaking wave, inviting disaster. And then it happened, as it always happened, just at the right moment, the last exquisite moment.

Their triumph. As old as time.

Acknowledgments

I'm told that authors of novels customarily thank only the muses for their divine inspiration. But I would like to thank some humans as well:

Dr. Allen S. Goldman, who gave so generously of his time and expertise when I visited him at the Children's Hospital of Philadelphia.

And Mort Janklow, Jerry Traum and Arthur Klebanoff, all of whom read and reread the manuscript, offering valuable suggestions as my book gradually came to life.

And friends—Georgeanne Heller, Stuart Berger, Rhoda Herrick and Stephen Landes, who, without reading a syllable, were there, offering food, shelter, shoulders, even extension cords for electric typewriters, but most of all the warmth of their friendship.

And Lorna Darmour, who read draft after draft, each time giving me the benefit of her fine sensibility and, as always, her boundless friendship.

And my parents, Lou and Sally Loeb, who, fifteen hundred miles away and without reading a word, were there, supportive as always and infuriatingly optimistic.

And Buz Wyeth of Harper & Row, who once again ventured into the unknown with me. How I treasure his wise counsel and constant encouragement.

And Burton Beals, who read each page, pen in hand, showing me how to make it better. And better.

To all of them, my love and my gratitude. The muses thank them too.